THE LONELY SICKNESS

THE LONELY SICKNESS

by Elizabeth D. Whitney

With a Preface by

Robert Fleming, M.D.

BEACON PRESS   BOSTON

Preface

In December, 1944, Mrs. Elizabeth Whitney brought together a group of prominent Boston professional and business people and organized them into the Boston Committee for Education on Alcoholism. This was the first voluntary community organization specializing in the problems of alcoholism, and Mrs. Whitney has been its energetic and resourceful executive director ever since.

It is out of innumerable interviews with alcoholic men and women and their families; hundreds of telephone calls and conferences; conversations with psychiatrists, social workers, clergymen, lawyers, legislators, industrialists, and teachers, that the material for this book has come. It is based upon the lives of many real men and women who are groping toward the insight which is a necessary initial part of treatment.

Mrs. Whitney has become wise in many aspects of alcoholism such as the problems of its occurrence in industry and the organization of community resources for helping the alcoholic, but above all she has become exceedingly expert in the problems of getting the individual alcoholic person, who is often acutely ill, frightened, confused, and embittered, into the hands of the proper agency for treatment. Needless to say this is a very important first step in the rehabilitation of any alcoholic, but it is also more than that; it is, itself, treatment.

The image of chronic alcohol poisoning which most people have is an incorrect one; this is particularly true of the alcoholic himself, who is often the last person to realize that he has become pathologically embroiled with alcohol and is losing his ability to control his drinking.

v

Alcoholism is a progressive illness of protean complexity, involving not only the body and mind of the afflicted individual but also his family and social relationships as a whole. Treatment of the alcoholic patient may call upon the enormous resources of medicine and psychiatry, of law and religion, but, boiled down to its essential core, treatment consists in bringing about a complete and permanent cessation of the alcoholic's use of alcohol. No matter what emotional or physical or social problems may remain unresolved, if the alcoholic stops drinking and stays abstinent he is successfully treated as far as his alcoholism is concerned; and, no matter what else may happen (improved physical and emotional health, better family and social relationships), if he continues to drink his treatment is a failure up to that point.

Unlike some of its predecessors this book does not attempt to add to the many theories about the "underlying causes of alcoholism." Mrs. Whitney has been too busy on the firing line helping actual people deal with actual troubles to indulge in armchair fantasies. The book is an important and valuable addition to the literature.

ROBERT FLEMING, M.D.

Acknowledgments

In the preparation and writing of this book I am indebted to many people. Not only have men and women with extraordinary professional skill in the healing arts helped me to bring hope and help to over ten thousand persons suffering from alcoholism but they have encouraged me to go on with the task of informing and educating the general public concerning the sickness.

My thanks is extended to the many men and women who confided to me the unvarnished details of their involvement, struggle and recovery. Few non-alcoholic people can appreciate the painful inner turmoil which, more than anything else, cries for a confidant. I have listened to them with respect for their courage and sympathy for their distress.

I am grateful to Robert Fleming, M.D., whose calm and dispassionate studies of alcoholism, from the earliest days of my interest in this field, have been of such great help to me in arriving at an understanding of a very complex disease, and whose generous preface introduces me to a new audience.

For my late husband, Lyman F. Whitney, who encouraged and supported my work in the voluntary health field, remembrance can never be adequate acknowledgment. He, with friends and counselors like Arthur T. Lyman, Palmer York, David Landau, M.D., Charles L. Powers, Courtney Baylor, William Philcrantz and Martha Brunner-Orne, M.D., have done so much to erase the stigma from alcoholism.

I am grateful to the men and women in Alcoholics Anonymous, whose serenity has been a mainstay of so many of the people I have tried to help.

Several eminent scientists and professional men who are no longer alive helped me to find acceptable answers to alcoholism problems which were far too baffling for a lay person. It is my hope that what Merrill Moore, M.D., Hans Sachs, Ph.D., and E. M. Jellinek, Sc.D., contributed to my small sum of knowledge about alcoholism has been put to use, which they would have approved.

For professional knowledge and skills as well as encouragement in the long task of organizing and writing this book I am deeply indebted to Lester Allen, Sr.

E.D.W.

Contents

THE LONELY SICKNESS

CHAPTER ONE

A Return from Fantasy

The call came late at night after Jan had fallen into a troubled sleep.

"I have a collect call for Mrs. Barrett. Is this Mrs. Barrett?" asked the operator. "Mr. William Barrett is calling from New Orleans. Will you accept charges?"

New Orleans! Jan was now fully awake. "Yes. Yes, put him on please. Put him on."

"Jan," a voice implored, "for God's sake come and get me. They're right outside the door, right outside."

She barely recognized her husband's voice, hoarse with hysteria and fear. "Bill! Is that you, Bill?"

"Jan, please, for God's sake. . . ."

"What—what are you doing in New Orleans, Bill?"

"Please, Jan, don't ask me questions. Just come and get me. They're right outside my door and they won't go away."

"Who's outside the door, Bill? I don't understand. Who is it?"

"Funny little men with big heads, funny little men."

There was more incoherent talk, more pleas for Jan to come immediately, as if New Orleans were just around the corner. She got from him the name of his hotel and she promised to get him—without having the faintest plan of how she would do it. She kept hearing his last despairing cry: "Jan, come to me. I need you!"

She placed a call to the house physician of the New Orleans hotel and, with an assumed calmness, asked for his help. Irritated by the lateness of the hour, the house doctor at first grumbled, "The man in 419. . . . Oh, yes. . . .

Well, Mrs. Barrett, I think I should tell you he's drunk, and I'd say he's having hallucinations."

The doctor's irritation seemed to wear off as he talked. He became the professional man, trying to communicate reassurance to a tense and anxious woman on the telephone.

"Believe me, Mrs. Barrett, we have done our best for him. I know a little bit about this, not only as a hotel physician seeing all sorts of emergency problems, but in my own practice I have treated several alcoholics. He's a sick man, and I don't mean just nauseated. I mean he is sick, suffering from an illness. He needs more help than I can give him. He needs long-term treatment. This isn't the hour of night to be discussing this over the phone; he needs not only treatment but also the help and understanding of someone near and dear to him."

"Will you see to it that he doesn't do anything to harm himself until I get there?"

"You are coming here . . . from Boston?" The house doctor sounded incredulous.

"Yes, I'm coming first thing in the morning."

"Well, I'll give him something to quiet him and I'll look in on him around noon. But what I give him won't be good for more than eight hours, if that long. How long will it take you to get here?"

"I don't know, but I'll start first thing in the morning. I'll get the first flight out of New York. Please try to keep him quiet until I get there."

There was no longer any doubt. Bill wasn't just an excessive drinker. He wasn't merely a gregarious man who liked drinking with friends. He was in trouble that he wouldn't admit or recognize. He had been struggling on alone, determined to preserve what he called his right to drink. Bill was out of control, huddled in sweating fear in a strange city.

This latest adventure in his life was a crisis that threatened Bill's job and family. Some kind of stand had to be taken. Bill had to be made to see what was wrong. However, Jan had doubts about her determination to take action. Bill would be contrite. She knew he would muster his reserve of personal charm and that teasing, evasive mock sincerity of his. He would state positively, "Jan, I've learned my lesson. No more. I'm through." It would go on this way—a deceitful accord between them for two months or so, and then, what she feared would happen again. He wouldn't be through with drinking. He would just be taking evasive action. This crisis would only lead to a whole new set of rationalizations. No. Not this time. She would be firm. This was the crucial time to take action.

But first, Jan had other problems to solve. She had a little cash, but not enough for a trip to New Orleans. There would be Bill's hotel bill, his fare home. She would need at least five hundred dollars. She couldn't ask his office for the money. This would expose Bill to awkward questions. Harry, her brother, was the only immediate prospect. But she couldn't wake him up in the middle of the night. He could get the money for her as soon as the bank opened. Heavens! it's Saturday. Well, he could get a check cashed because he managed the big hardware store and had to have change. His wife would object. She'd make it difficult because she really didn't like Bill. But this was an emergency and Jan had asked only once before for help—the time Bill ran into the post at the intersection and wrecked the car. She would call Harry around breakfast time.

Jimmy and Sarah! They were away at school, but they would be coming home the following week for the Easter vacation. What if they telephoned while she was away? She couldn't upset their visit with her trouble with their father. Harry could explain it. She'd ask him to call them. They would accept an explanation from their uncle. These were her thoughts as she packed a small bag for the trip to New Orleans.

In New Orleans, Jan saw the house doctor before she went to Bill's room. He was frank and spared no details.

"I must tell you, Mrs. Barrett, he's a sick man. I've given him paraldehyde and that's all he's had. He was trying to stop drinking when he got here. Anyway, we shut him off. No liquor at all, and that's why he went into withdrawal symptoms—seeing things. He's in trouble with liquor."

"Yes, I know," she murmured, "I know that. I've known it for some time."

"Do you do very much of this—running around to rescue him?"

"No, never before. I don't understand why he came to New Orleans."

"He doesn't either, so don't try to find out. Just get him home and try to get some treatment for him. He's all right to travel—shaky and jittery, but he can make it."

"Thank you, I must go up to his room and see him."

"By the way, do you know what paraldehyde smells like?"

"No."

"Well, it's pungent, but that's all you'll smell in his room. It's not liquor. We cleaned the bottles out two days ago. I'm glad you came for him."

Bill was partially dressed, pacing the floor when she knocked at the door. He hadn't shaved. His face was puffy and his hands shook.

Jan attempted to be matter-of-fact, to tell Bill without emotion what the doctor had told her. The man who had pleaded with her to come and get him, who had said that he needed her, didn't embrace her, didn't kiss her, but stood with the bed between them, his head turned away from the light streaming in the windows.

"D.T.'s!" he exclaimed when Jan told him he had been having hallucinations. He arranged his puffed features in what he felt to be an expression of astonishment and dismay.

"Who told you a story like that? I just had a severe gastric upset. Ask the house doctor. He'll tell you that I had been drinking, sure, but a gastric upset was the real trouble. It was probably the shellfish I ate for lunch. Jan, I give you my word, I was delirious with the pain and my heart was acting in a funny way. So don't pay too much attention to what I said on the phone. Don't hold that against me. A man in deep pain can't be expected to talk calmly and rationally."

"Oh, Bill, it won't do. You were never in New Orleans in your life before. I don't think you even remember coming here."

"Now Jan, please give me credit. I should have phoned to tell you what I was doing. But I got a big deal going here, something that will mean big things in our future. I had to strike while the iron was hot. So I just flew down here with a couple of men in the group to smooth out details."

He went on, dropping names, embroidering a story he hoped she would accept and, if it worked with her, he could use at the office to account for his absence. He embellished the story with half truths and vague references to business contacts. His lips were dry and his eyes were tortured, but he went on.

How brave, she thought. How foolish. Her heart felt pain at his desperation.

Several times on the flight back to Boston she was almost at the point of accepting the falsehoods if only to save his pride, but looking at his trembling fingers as he lit a cigarette, the tremor of his mouth and hands as he tried to drink coffee, reinforced her conviction that Bill was not only sick, physically and mentally, but that his denial of the sickness was one of the symptoms of his disease.

Her brother's words, "Jan, do something about him. Don't let it go another day. Do something. Divorce him if you have to, but don't let him destroy all of you."

The day after their return from New Orleans, while their family doctor was reinforcing Bill's alibi that he had suffered a severe gastric upset, Jan telephoned my office and asked if she could talk with someone about a problem—a drinking problem.

"Actually," she said, "it's my husband. He doesn't admit that he has a drinking problem. But certain things have happened that disturb me. . . . My brother insists on my taking some action. I heard your radio program and I discussed it with our doctor. He knew of you and your work and suggested I see you, so I thought I'd ask what could be done. . . . Please understand, he doesn't look like an alcoholic. . . ."

I refrained from asking her what an alcoholic looks like.

She was tall and fair and she seemed reasonably calm when she appeared for her appointment. It was obvious that she had lived with extreme anxiety for at least a few days. She was diffident about discussing her husband's behavior with a stranger. She sat looking submissive and plainly waiting for me to judge a problem, the details of which she hadn't revealed.

"Why don't you tell me something about yourself and your husband, and about when and how he drinks. Perhaps we can develop something from that," I said.

She sat erect, tapping her cigarette lightly at the ash tray. She started with the telephone call in the middle of the night, the frantic trip to New Orleans, the smell of paraldehyde in the hotel room, Bill's shaking hands and his tortured eyes.

"You love him and want to help him?" I asked.

"Yes, I think I do."

"Then let's see what we can do. Tell me about his drinking behavior, his background, and yours too."

"I have tried to hide what it was," she said, "but everyone will know soon. Not even I can hide it any longer. I've tried, but it hasn't worked. I've covered for him with friends. I've kept it from the children. I even sent them away to school so they wouldn't know what I was going through. They can't have their friends at the house any more because I never know when their father will come home drunk.

"His boss knows something is wrong. When I call in to say Bill is ill there's something in his tone. . . . Bill drinks too much at business meetings. When he has a few drinks he waves his arms around in big gestures. I know he talks too much at business meetings. He's going to lose his job, I just know it, even though he's the best salesman they have.

"There's been some trouble about his expense accounts, but I don't know where the money goes. I just about meet the bills. If he loses his job we'll have to let the house go and we'll have to take the children out of school. What will we do then? Perhaps I should have listened to my brother and his wife a year ago when they advised me to leave him. But I think that they resent the way he treats them and talks to them. Bill jeers at the hardware business and he makes cracks about provincial dullards and things like that.

"This seems to be the end . . . but he has talked our doctor into believing that he had a gastric attack while he was out of town on business. He is such a good salesman. He can even sell our doctor a story like that."

The story Mrs. Barrett told is common. I have heard it with variations many times, sometimes not so grim, but often a complicated synopsis of tragedy. Alcoholism affects different people differently because it is an individual, personalized disease, having a certain similarity to other sets of symptoms, but never identical in its progress toward the chronic stages. The line separating heavy social drinking from alcoholism is difficult to see (except under precise clinical conditions). Alcoholics are also ingenious at compensating for changes in their behavior so that modifications of basic character can go on for years and the changes can be attributed to the process of aging.

Jan had passed from concern for Bill in her recital to concern for herself. "What's going to happen to me? I've got to think about that. Do you think Bill is a hopeless alcoholic?"

"No alcoholic is truly hopeless. From what you have told me so far your husband seems to have passed the early stage of alcoholism and is now in what is generally called the middle phase. I think if I describe what you have told me in terms of progressive symptoms you can identify certain milestones in his progress into the middle phase."

I explained to Jan that the first phase, technically called the prodromal or forerunning symptoms, usually shows a gradual change from the moderate use of alcohol on social occasions to use of increasing amounts on every occasion. This may mean more frequent drinking occasions or increasing amounts of alcohol being *needed* to achieve the same feeling of well-being or euphoria once gained from less frequent drinking occasions and smaller amounts of alcohol. Euphoria becomes more desirable to the first stage alcoholic than the social lubrication that aids in good fellowship, relaxation, and loosened inhibitions when a drink or two is taken in company. In the first stages of alcoholism the person headed for trouble will seek and find reasons to justify the amounts he drinks. Added to this early symptom, which can be observed by relatives and intimates, are periodic blackouts in which the early alcoholic walks, talks, and behaves naturally, even without staggering. He will not remember specific behavior or what has taken place over periods of time ranging from a few minutes to hours while drinking. Technically a blackout is alcoholic amnesia.

In the first phase the alcoholic will be able to drink larger quantities of alcohol without changing his personality. His tissues demand and tolerate more alcohol to achieve the euphoria he experienced earlier on fewer drinks. Then small changes in personality will be noticed while an alcoholic is drinking.

Jan's nod, while I was explaining alcoholic behavior during the first phases, indicated that she recognized the symptoms.

"This seems an excellent time to offer your husband help," I told her. "No matter how he tries to minimize the crisis, he is acutely aware of it. He is frightened and wonders what is going to happen to him. He is going through some shattering experiences in the present middle phase.

"In the middle phase an alcoholic no longer drinks entirely for social purposes; he drinks because he has to drink in order to maintain physical and emotional equilibrium. Once he takes a drink he is unable to stop for reasons of social acceptability or prudence. Alcoholics Anonymous members describe this as 'one drink is too many and a hundred is never enough.' The feeling of well-being once so desirable now eludes him. He pursues the lost euphoria, grasping it only momentarily. More and more he has woven around himself and his life a network of rationalizations to justify his drinking and to account for behavior that even he recognizes as extraordinary. He has grandiose ideas which seem to others like outrageous romancing or fourflushing. To him fantasy has become reality. He awakens from troubled sleep physically distressed and mentally jaded, and threatened by a hangover of such intensity that he cannot face it and function normally or even near normally. And so he has to have a drink. And this is a cumulative compulsion, driving him on until he stumbles into a crisis such as Bill experienced. By sheer will power he has managed to preserve an outward face of stereotyped calmness through all this buildup of tension, while inside were terror and tension and anxiety which he could hold in check only by more and more of the 'medicine' he has discovered will soothe his pain. He sees any treatment which deprives him of drinking as taking away the only medicine he knows will work. This is why he tries to defend himself, why he creates alibis to justify his behavior. If help is offered to him now, in spite of his efforts to convince your family doctor that he has had only a gastric upset, he will at least look into it. We can go on from there.

"Don't expect your husband to change his accumulated behavior patterns overnight. He has been building them up for years. The change will come slowly, but you can help him, and you can watch the changes take place. . . ."

"What should we do?" she asked.

We. That was the clue I was waiting for. Once again she thought of the problem in terms of us. We would take it from there.

Jan's attitude was not the usual one. Many wives submit to the incessant brainwashings alcoholics use in defense of their behavior. They are often personally reluctant to believe that the real trouble with a husband is simply that he drinks compulsively and is an alcoholic.

She had noted the alibis, the efforts of Bill to defend himself and protect his drinking, even the family physician's tongue-in-cheek acceptance of the mysterious gastric upsets. But Jan really hadn't been deceived. Few wives can bring their exasperation and disillusionment under control. The usual reaction of a wife to her husband's alcoholism will be recognized by a marriage counsellor. Either the wife is long-suffering and adopts a resigned attitude, or is indignant and argues that she is right and her husband is wrong.

The complexities of alcoholic symptoms and alcoholic behavior are the main factors in the misunderstanding between family members. Wives and other family members strive to account for the behavior of an alcoholic by applying simple standards of right and wrong. Often the last thing they consider is that they are dealing with a sickness, an addiction to a drug that gains a powerful ascendancy over an alcoholic.

Alcohol has a powerful anesthetic effect. It is a depressant, not a stimulant. This is how alcohol acts in the human body to produce the effect desired by the majority of social drinkers (over 80 million adults in the United States).

In an age when tension controlling drugs are being synthesized and drugs have been used to summon hallucinations from the subconscious, alcohol seems a tame drug indeed. Many regard it as no more dangerous than the simplest home remedy and infinitely more palatable.

Most doctors will agree that if alcohol were discovered today it would be hailed as a medical advance. It would take a long time to discover the side effect of addiction that it holds for some people. Alcohol seems a gift of Nature derived from a natural process of fermentation, harmful only to those who abuse it. It was accepted as such by generation after generation, even though the ancients discovered a malign influence in wine for some—and only some—of those who drank too deeply. How alcohol can enslave some and spare the majority has remained a mystery down to modern times. It was a mystery explained away by moral judgments and codified precepts forbidding overindulgence. It still afforded those immune to the addictive nature of alcohol the boon of temporary relief from anxiety and tension.

Development of the disease concept is making headway against accumulated misinformation and prejudice. With an alcoholic's relatives, one can never be certain where to begin, for they may have older moralistic viewpoints about the disease.

Jan had accepted the idea that alcoholism is a sickness and that she would have to take part in the treatment in some way, but she was not aware that her role was to be almost passive, carrying through a studied behavior that

would be an almost complete switch from her previous attitude. The man she had solemnly pledged to cherish in sickness and in health would get well only if she followed in-
structions and left the therapy to those who were not emotionally linked to her husband. They would convince the
patient that he was curing himself, that he alone would be
responsible for his recovery. Her reward would be the res-
toration of the man she married and loved enough to want
him to get well.

"Yes," Jan said, "he's very sick, I agree, but what can
I do to understand what kind of a sickness it is? He has to
live in our neighborhood among our friends and work at his
job. Sick people get some treatment. How do I explain this
to myself? Because you tell me it is important to understand
that what is wrong with him is alcoholism? What is alcoholism? Why don't all our drinking friends become alcoholics? Why just Bill?"

I didn't attempt to answer those questions immediately.
"Is he willing to talk to someone about the situation? Does
he want to do something about his sickness?"

"I told him I can't go on this way and the children's
lives are going to be spoiled. He asked me what I want him
to do, and said he'll do whatever I say. I can tell him I want
him to see you, first of all."

"I'd rather you didn't say that. I'd rather you say that
you would like him to come with you to get some information about the problem, and then I can try to take it from
there."

Jan went away with two booklets describing the elements of family concern about alcoholism. She said she
would telephone for an appointment.

When she phoned she had Bill at her side. He had a
deep voice with a humorous inflection.

"Let's see what we can come up with," he said after he

had been introduced over the phone. Bill was trying to set up an interview on his terms.

"Yes," I answered, "that would be good. I'm sure that you will come up with something that will be helpful."

Bill had taken the first step to accept responsibility for his own rehabilitation.

CHAPTER TWO

Alcoholism—What Is It?

A simple definition of alcoholism is necessary for discussion of the problem. The encyclopedic *Classified Abstract of Literature on Alcoholism* contains 187 different definitions, varying in some slight degree of emphasis on physiological or psychological symptoms, but all dependent upon the special attitude and knowledge of the person who formulated each. Alcoholism can very easily create a whole system of medical polemics because it is a highly personalized disease fitting the contours of the individual patient's body and mind like an astronaut's pressure suit. The definition that fits one may seem inapt applied to another.

The essential elements of alcoholism are found in the use of alcoholic beverages that cause the individual trouble in family, economic, spiritual, social, physical, and mental areas.

Many attempts have been made to chart the progressive symptoms of alcoholism. They are usually depicted as a downward curve appropriately labeled at various hypothetical stages of involvement. The trouble with such formulations of symptoms is that not only the alcoholic but also those observing the onset of the disease seize those symptoms they haven't observed or experienced as positive proof that alcoholism in their case can be ruled out. "He can't be an alcoholic," they may say, "because he goes to his job every day."

Alcohol's effect on those who use it is identical with the effect of an anesthetic. Its usefulness as a beverage has a venerable history. One in every fourteen drinkers in North America—about 6 percent of the total population—is adversely affected by the use of alcohol. Once they begin to use alcohol obsessively they are called alcoholics, an unfortunate stigmatic name for which no substitute has yet been found.

For the thirteen other drinkers alcohol is a useful element of social life fully accepted in our society even though the majority who use it are aware of the risk of addiction. Addiction to alcohol is marked by increasingly serious damage to the individual's personality, his physical and psychological functioning, and his judgment about personal decisions and interpersonal relationships.

Put more simply, alcoholism is a progressive condition of illness affecting the total functioning of the individual. Often this progression is so gradual that the illness is uncontrollable for as long as the patient continues to drink.

To say that alcohol does not cause alcoholism is to indulge in a subtlety of semantics. Diseases in general have causes and effects. They show manifestations of agent, host, and vector (carrier), or if not infectious a combination of physiological and psychological conditions that disturb the balanced functioning of the individual.

Tuberculosis, for example, develops through interaction of agent, host, and carrier which permits the tuberculosis bacilli to invade the victim's tissues.

Diabetes, on the other hand, closer akin to alcoholism in its irreversible aspects, shows an agent—sugar, a host—the victim's tissues, and a condition of the pancreas that raises the sugar content of the blood.

Not all people are vulnerable to tuberculosis bacilli or to diabetes or to alcoholism.

Those who do not contract tuberculosis, even if exposed to a carrier, repel the bacillus, or encapsulate it if it gains entry to their tissues. Those who do not contract diabetes regardless of sugar intake produce enough insulin in the pancreas to convert the sugar. Those who do not develop alcoholism are invulnerable to the toxic effect of alcohol, which in alcoholics first builds up and then breaks down tissue tolerance, and by progressive steps results in obsessive drinking.

Regardless of how long or how short a time it takes for the alcoholic to develop obsessive drinking, one thing is manifest to those who observe the onset of alcoholism in individuals—they are not the same people they were before alcoholism developed. They have shown changes in their behavior.

The recovery of alcoholics must necessarily be a prolonged process because they must develop or reconstitute a set of values that will somewhere ahead allow them to rejoin the main highway of the life they left for the bypath of alcoholism. Today the intervention of treatment usually occurs during the middle phase of the disease. By the time this middle phase of alcoholism has been reached the alcoholic has developed a very complex pattern of concern, concealment, and indecision that further complicates what might otherwise be a simple abnormality of the individual's metabolism of alcohol. In the middle phase of alcoholism, as noted by the late E. M. Jellinek, the alcoholic most commonly seen clinically in the United States has developed increased tissue tolerance for alcohol, requiring more alcohol to achieve the same level of euphoria. In withdrawal such alcoholics experience acute physiological disturbances, tremors, gastritis, and an acute need for more alcohol to suppress the symptoms. It is manifest to those who treat alcoholics that if these were the only symptoms it would be possible to treat this abnormality of the metabolic setup of alcoholics as an acute physical symptom entirely, but the extraordinary complexity of the psychological symptoms interwoven with the physical symptoms make treatment a task for a team of therapists representing a wide range of healing disciplines.

Doctors are not happy with the operational evaluations

of alcoholism that are in use as definitions because they cover such a wide range of social and cultural factors that modify or intensify the effect of alcoholism on the individual. But the fact that alcoholism is so conspicuous in all social and economic categories of people and in all our contemporary cultures makes it imperative that as in navigation in ancient times therapists must still strive to reach a haven of sobriety for their patients by guess and by God. They also realize there will be no lack of subjects to aid in the study of the variables that make every case of alcoholism unique. Alcohol spares from addiction all but one in every fourteen to sixteen social drinkers, so that given a figure of an approximate number of social drinkers in any definite locality one can project with reasonable accuracy the number of alcoholics in that locality.

Regardless of one's personal bias concerning the use of alcoholic beverages there are certain undeniable effects to be gained from its use in moderation for those who do not become addicted. Alcohol works quickly in the body as a tranquilizer, sedative, and anesthetic—faster indeed than any other pleasure-giving substance. The majority of drinkers use alcohol for social reasons because it is the thing to do in their group, or to make them feel that they belong, or to forget the tensions of everyday living, or to feel relaxed, or to mark a festive occasion. Alcoholics drink differently. Their use of alcohol makes it a toxic substance, a drug, something they cannot live with or without, that affects their finances, their family, their health, their skill or profession.

Alcoholic beverages get their stamp of approval from people themselves, from their frequent everyday references to it. Drinking has acquired a vast descriptive synonymy—shot, highball, pick-me-up, cocktail, bang, lift, blast, slug, sauce, and the like—all carrying the implication that liquor lifts up or stimulates. Today's drinking culture, borrowed from drinking cultures of the past, stresses health and friendly intercourse between people sharing an uplifting experience.

It has long been known to investigators of alcohol problems that while alcoholics dispose of alcohol by the same process of metabolism as do nonalcoholics, some irreversible changes occur in alcoholics' cells. The role of enzymes in alcoholism seems to investigators to be vital because if an enzyme necessary to a chemical step in metabolism of alcohol is missing, illness or addiction may ensue. Investigation of these abnormalities of the metabolic process and consequent changes in cells continues. When Alcoholics Anonymous was founded in 1935 alcoholism was described as an allergy of the body and an obsession of the mind. This concept expressed the feelings of alcoholics seriously pondering their addiction to alcohol. They felt that they were powerless over alcohol because of some abnormality in the way their bodies utilized alcohol. The allergy concept was discarded as scientific investigation progressed.

Causes of alcoholism are now being pursued by biochemists with the framework in mind of the work on diabetes, which centered upon the metabolism of sugar. The basic reasons why the faulty metabolism of alcohol by certain individuals should produce a behavioral disorder are still actively sought.

It is not surprising therefore that the true action of alcohol in the human body is completely misunderstood. Human behavior has certain mechanisms familiar to physiologists, neurologists, and psychiatrists, who are concerned with the part that inhibition plays in development and control of human behavior. But inhibitions are not completely understood by the layman.

Take the quiet businessman who at a cocktail party capers around wearing a lampshade for a hat. Normally his inhibitions would say, "Don't be ridiculous." But his judgment and inhibitory centers have been affected by the alcohol circulating in the blood to his brain, bringing out the clown in him. His inhibitions give no stern command to control himself. And so he pops the shade on his head and gets a laugh from his drinking companions.

Social poise does not come as a built-in attribute in people. The precise balance of reserve and openness approved as desirable by society requires training and rules. In consequence we have at all levels of social intercourse people who are either too extroverted or too introverted to be comfortably adjusted to their milieu. Here is the point where the effect of alcohol performs a useful function. The wallflower loses timidity or diffidence. The inarticulate find their tongues. The dull become sparkling, at least in their mind's eye. Animation comes to the passive. Some of the most retiring people become about as shy as an avalanche.

It is this effect of alcohol that becomes not only meaningful but essential to the alcoholic. The normal social drinker experiences the phenomenon of release from inhibitions with no special response or extraordinary valuation other than the temporary easing of the onerous routine of living. This release, a feeling of freedom, has a special meaning for the person who eventually becomes an alcoholic. This special meaning is not at first apparent.

What is noted by the potential alcoholic is that release from inhibitions is certain and that it can be prolonged beyond the brief social hour. The crucial matters of human relationships—ranging from wooing to working—seem to go better after a drink or two.

The process of becoming addicted to the drug that produces this effect is slow and often imperceptible. The orientation of the individual changes by small degrees. More to drink is required to bring about the desired release. Drinking occasions gradually become more important and exclude other forms of social activity.

Added to the change of orientation is a seeming social desirability and success. So-and-so is a good fellow, and a desirable drinking companion. A woman, pursuing the popularity she has experienced while drinking, is considered to be good fun. Who gives up this much-to-be-desired social success to become dull inarticulate me again?

The new man and the new woman created by the illusion of release are desirable people. Buy the new man (or the new woman) another drink.

By inexorable stages their lives become reoriented to the use of liquor in all situations of stress—physical, psychological, social, or economic. Yet they have no available means of measuring the degree of their involvement in alcoholism or for that matter any persuasive and overwhelming proof of the gravity of their illness.

Drinkers and nondrinkers, social drinkers and alcoholics, share an attitude of extreme skepticism about the disease concept of alcoholism, but for different reasons. Their common doubts are illustrated best in their invariable demand for a definition of alcoholism. They want precise instruction on the difference between an abstainer, a social drinker, an excessive social drinker, and an alcoholic, usually with some degree of moralistic conviction expressed.

If one explores the considered judgment of nonalcoholic drinkers one is certain to find as many oversimplifications, rationalizations, myths, old wives' tales, fuzzy aphorisms, and sheer nonsense about alcoholic beverages as one finds in the thinking of an alcoholic.

Few nonalcoholics ask themselves what a drink seems to do for them and to them. They are certain that they know what it does for them—usually saying that it stimulates and relaxes. Yet they have no sound answer why they use alcoholic beverages at all.

Their belief that alcohol is a stimulant is shared by a majority of drinkers. It isn't; it's a depressant. But, they will argue after a highball their judgment is always keener, their perception sharper, their reactions swifter. It is simply not true. Scientific investigation shows that their judgment is impaired perceptibly, their reaction time is longer, their inhibitions are loosed. The important point is that their feeling of well-being has deceived them.

Reasons why they drink at all are part of their self-deception. They drink to relax after a trying day, to sharpen a jaded appetite, to celebrate an occasion, to seal a bargain, to cement a friendship, to medicate for some ailment, to fortify against cold, to get relief from excessive heat, to console themselves, to express their joy, and so on through a long list of rationalizations that man, finding enjoyment in the use of alcohol, has dreamed up to keep a firm grip on his capering inhibitions. Such a leash indicates that man has known for thousands of years that alcohol, unless sternly controlled, can be a false friend, and that some are cruelly betrayed.

Yet nonalcoholics, and nondrinkers too, exclude from their consideration the distress of the alcoholic, the false logic of an alcoholic's rationalizations, which are those generally in use by all. The orientation of the lives of the majority of people to the use of liquor makes detection of the symptoms of alcoholism easier, even when the alcoholic carries on an elaborate masquerade as a social drinker, resisting any suggestion that the preferred use of alcohol shown by the alcoholic is very different from that of the normal social drinker.

Relatives and close associates can observe the telltale signs. The alcoholic makes tentative efforts, always futile, to give up heavy drinking and to drink more nearly like his nonalcoholic friends in his social group. Beer or wine may be substituted for whiskey, or tall drinks for full strength shots of whiskey on the rocks. Efforts are undertaken to abstain for varying periods of time—a week or two, until the next holiday, or during Lent. The motives for these efforts are carefully concealed by what the alcoholic believes are rational explanations of his efforts to quit.

These periods of sobriety are not truly a structured decision to make the effort to recover from alcoholism. Usually such episodes are for the purpose of deceiving oneself, one's wife or family, one's fellow employees, employer, or colleagues. These are showpieces of behavior, demonstrations of a false mastery of a drinking problem, staged with the intention of retaining in secret the use of alcohol as a tranquillizer. Sometimes these demonstrations may be staged at such jolly occasions as holidays, weddings, birthdays, anniversary parties, and office parties.

Sometimes such swearing off or abstaining is accompanied by an effort to reestablish status as an effective worker and an effective person. Remember that Bill Barrett had some vague idea of a big deal he was going to pull off in New Orleans. This was his rationalization to justify another serious drinking episode in his own mind and cover up his failure to remain sober.

Alcoholics frequently employ what seems to them to be slick psychology—the "swearing off" ploy—in which they publicly declare they have been drinking too much, they are going to quit; but this is underlaid by their plan to change their pattern of drinking and conceal the fact that they are in the clutches of a true addiction.

What the alcoholic is saying by this adroit show of good intentions is, "See, I am able to stop drinking. I can refuse a drink. I can go for a week (or a month) or more without touching a drop. Therefore I am not an alcoholic. I'm not like the people you condemn as alcoholics."

Application of the true test of whether or not alcoholism is the real trouble is avoided by alcoholics until circumstances, or combinations of circumstances, force them to face what is to them the ugly truth—once they start drinking they cannot stop until they come up against an insurmountable barrier to further drinking. This barrier could be the intervention of another person, lack of money, acute sickness, arrest, an accident, or restraint of one kind or another over which they personally have no control. In Bill Barrett's case the meaningful crisis was an attack of D.T.'s.

More often than the general public suspects, physicians and family discover the true state of affairs only when the alcoholic is hospitalized and unable to secure liquor, with the result that withdrawal symptoms occur.

Alcoholics cannot be decisive about their disease or about taking the step that will control it for the rest of their lives because of the subtle onset of their dependency on alcohol. The length of time that elapses between the beginning of regular social drinking and the onset of the serious and damaging symptoms of alcoholism establishes drinking as the central social fact of the alcoholic's life. Generally, the alcoholic's preferred social group is a drinking group. Successful men and women in that group drink socially, so the alcoholic wants to know why he can't drink socially. The alcoholic only breaks bonds with such a group when concealment of his disease becomes a desperate necessity, when the acceptance and approbation of the group is consciously withheld because of the alcoholic's drinking behavior. Then he is condemned. Active alcoholics look bleakly and despairingly at a future in which they can never again partake of alcohol. It is far easier to be self-deceiving and cling to the belief that one is still a social drinker and remain in or near a prestige drinking group.

One of the recovered alcoholics who reviewed his drinking history for me gave a touching illustration of this aspect of the alcoholic's resistance to accepting the fact that he is an alcoholic. "My drinking group was limited. I wasn't a barroom drinker. I went around a lot with my crowd. I felt secure with them. I know now that they were distressed by the way I drank and wanted to say something to me about it. But they couldn't because they drank with me. It took a long time for me to realize that I wasn't invited any more, that my posing as a social drinker, my tricks to drink a lot while they drank a little weren't fooling anyone. But I felt that I was a drowning man and they were beating me across the knuckles to make me let go of their boat when they got rid of me. But I didn't stop drinking. What I did was to pretend that I wasn't drinking any more, and I drank alone or with strangers, and I made cracks where they could hear me about how they were a bunch of lushes. I wanted to revenge myself, not stop myself."

Acceptable public attitudes are at odds with the actualities of alcoholism. The stigma on alcoholics persists even though lip service is given to the disease concept. Perhaps the real responsibility for the persistent stigma may be said to lie with the alcoholic, who seeks concealment, isolation, or a permissive drinking group, rather than be labeled a drunkard or an alcoholic, or both, by his own set. The alcoholic thus reinforces the moral judgments of the people around him by his efforts to pretend that nothing is amiss in his drinking behavior.

In this social dilemma the alcoholic may attempt to find ways of concealment which, because of his impaired judgment, are so obvious that they automatically classify themselves. Sometimes in the deep trouble of a drinking episode they will seek the companionship of those humble and tragic misfits in the low places on Skid Row. As companions, the uncomplicated but predatory Skid Row drinkers neither condemn nor reject. The passport into their world is a shared bottle. This expedient is not, however, acceptable to the vast majority of alcoholics, and only 3 percent of the nation's active alcoholics are on Skid Row.

Solitary drinking is the usual alternative. The binge starts with a few drinks with the familiar social group in a familiar social situation, and it proceeds through a retreat into isolation and concealment—a hotel room, a motel, a summer cottage, a camp, in bars not usually frequented by friends. As the binge proceeds the alcoholic uses less and less caution about possible disclosure. Often repeated, incoherent telephone calls to friends will disclose the fact that an individual is in the grip of this disease. Telephonitis is a true symptom of alcoholism.

Telephonitis does not occur to all alcoholics, but to the majority who are accustomed when sober to use the telephone on regular social or business calls, it is a frequently observed symptom. The telephone provides a means of remaining isolated while drinking and yet reaching out to maintain contact with people in the desperation of loneliness. Some bizarre examples of telephonitis are a part of the recollections of a significantly large group of recovered alcoholics. Time and distance have no meaning to the alcoholic in the throes of telephonitis. They would as soon call Bangkok as Boston. People they haven't seen in years may be startled out of bed in the middle of the night. And they hear a fuzzy voice saying, "I was thinking about you and thought I'd give you a call."

One alcoholic who ran up telephone bills that surely made him the best single customer of the Bell system became internationally famous as the National Disturbance Corporation. The famous and infamous would be roused in the small hours of the morning to hear, "This is Mr. Flopoor of the National Disturbance Corporation calling. Are you disturbed?" When he finally achieved secure sobriety and ceased his telephonic heckling, he turned his wildly imaginative and articulate ability on the telephone to good account and made clients for a telephone survey service of many of the famous people he had heckled. It would not have been unusual to find that Mr. Barrett did a lot of this kind of telephoning.

Alcoholics who cannot hide away when they are in the

midst of a drinking episode go through a rigorous type of drinking training, self-taught, that requires the exercise of immense will power and strict attention to the precise limits of their tissue tolerance for alcohol. This involves maintaining an intake of alcohol that will keep them contented, and present an illusion of being with it, but which will at the same time blunt the sharp spears of reality. Many working alcoholics manage this kind of drinking week in and week out with their intake increasing ever so gradually until at last they reach the end of physical and psychological reserves.

A study of this pacing of alcoholic intake carried out with a group of ten active alcoholics showed that they had the ability to function with an intake of 30 ounces of whiskey a day, spread over twenty-four hours.* This amount of alcohol maintained a blood alcohol level that was fairly low and therefore unusual. Had they been doing the same sort of controlled drinking without supervision they would have experienced gratification of their increasing need for slightly more liquor each day until they would have come to a physical crisis and very high blood alcohol levels. It is a demonstrated fact that an alcoholic can exercise rigid self-control within certain limits, which belies the oft-repeated assertion of those who are not familiar with alcoholics that they have no will power. It requires a supreme exercise of will power to limit the intake of alcohol when one's whole being cries out for more.

While alcoholism is a personalized illness with symptoms that are often unique in an individual there are certain milestones or benchmarks by which one can establish probabilities that will add up to a case of alcoholism.

Social drinking occasions give the first inkling. Alcoholics seek to prolong the drinking and to reject concomitant

---

* "Study of chronic induced intoxication and withdrawal." Mendelson et al.—Supplement—*Quarterly Journal of Studies in Alcohol,* 1964.

social activities. They seek opportunities for drinking. They prefer to pour their own drinks. They prepare for a social drinking occasion by putting down a foundation of a couple of drinks. They experience blackouts, or alcoholic amnesia, when they cannot recall what they have done and said for periods of time ranging from a couple of hours to a whole night. They fail to appear at their jobs, giving excuses that may seem reasonable and logical until the excuses are subjected to closer scrutiny. For example, how does a person recover overnight from severe bronchitis? Or how does a sprained ankle mend in twenty-four hours with a limp that shows only·when the sprainee remembers to limp? Do all sicknesses happen after weekends?

It is significant when a normally prudent person shows evidence of grandiose behavior, spending money needed for something else of greater necessity on prolonged drinking, or on efforts of one kind or another to acquire status in one's social group as a host or guest—always connected with drinking. Assuredly it was an alcoholic who first called for another cup of wine for everybody.

As the drinker joins the inexorable march of the disease, swept along by an increasing throng of compulsions, the pretensions that have blinded a family to the true state of affairs are stripped away. The family is first to know, among all the people who will eventually recognize that something is wrong with the way the alcoholic drinks. Not the least puzzling factor to them will be that among the majority of alcoholics the capacity for drinking is usually greater than average. It will have been said many times in the family that the drinker in their household can certainly hold his liquor, or that the usual aftereffects do not seem as severe. He or she can get up and go to work after a rough night. This rationalization is due to the alcoholic's determined efforts to conceal the physical symptoms and distress so that no chink in his armor of concealment can be found.

Yet family members become aware that something is
wrong. They experience a kind of extrasensory perception.
Those who share their lives feel the vibrations of the alcoholics' deep disquiet, their desperately hidden knowledge
that they do not drink as other social drinkers do. An alcoholic in the midst of a drinking episode is ultra sensitive.
They project emotions with far greater intensity, even
though the emotions are bent to the stark necessity of continuing to drink.

It has been noted that alcoholics are reluctant to face
up to the obvious facts about their condition, and that they
resist doing anything about their sickness until some serious
crisis develops. This is not entirely true in all cases of alcoholism however.

Alcoholics employ rationalizations and face-saving attitudes that are also present in the normal behavior of people
who do not have drinking problems. Everyone in some
degree seeks to justify behavior that he is aware is not
praiseworthy. And so with alcoholics their inner convictions
that something is wrong about their drinking behavior are
firmly suppressed to save face and to protect their use of
alcohol, which has become an essential medicine to them.
Bill Barrett's pretense that he had only experienced a gastric
upset is an example. This effort to reject the very clues that
might convince them that they are alcoholics does not in any
way alter the deep disturbing awareness that something is
seriously wrong with the way they drink. Whether this inner uneasiness will prompt them to seek help or advice de-
pends entirely upon the values by which they live.

Some people have in the forefront of their thinking love
of family, job interest, professional pride, even a desire to
spare others pain. Their judgment and inhibitions constantly
prick them and prompt them to face the fact that something
is seriously amiss. And they are in a way fortunate to have
what has been inspiringly described as a small bird of warn-

ing. The bird of warning pecks at their awareness until by choice or crisis they must ask for advice and help. And directly or indirectly they must act upon the disturbing information they get. At least they know beyond any reasonable doubt that they are alcoholics and that they will need help to control their disease. (These types can be helped sooner by wives and husbands, or other family members, who should recognize at this point that they should suggest looking into educational guides about alcoholism and avoid progressive development of its later and more serious states.)

By an identical set of values used by nonalcoholics, alcoholics have developed a false rationale about drinking. They too must have acceptable reasons to drink even though it is in a way that is quite different from the way nonalcoholics drink. Their compelling need for reasons that society will accept sends them on excursions into emotional cul-de-sacs and into unproductive or neurotic bypaths.

They map out a geography, an economic system, a history, a set of laws—a whole culture of a fanciful land in which they can exist in the guise of social drinkers. It is a land whose history is spangled with brave deeds of a heroic, gifted, brilliant people who have never existed except fleetingly in the brief exultation of intoxication. The burial grounds of that land are filled with monuments to dead aspirations and hopes.

Fundamental reasons for alcoholism are almost always found in individuals' environments where the real reasons for compulsive drinking first ensnared them, and where they first began adoption of an artful philosophy whose falsity would offer concealment, compromise, and comfort. The major premise of their cramped logic is that they too are social drinkers, and that by some impending alteration of their way of living they will be able to continue social drinking without the complications that now spoil their enjoyment.

They believe that their trouble with drink stems from many causes; from being unlucky, from the hostility of others, from inability to command the attention they deserve, from the general cussedness of people in their immediate circle, from the kind or brand of liquor they have been drinking, from any number of half-true or completely immature conceptions; but seldom do they face the fact that they are sick and have chosen a medicine for their ailment that can only aggravate their condition.

Basically their aim in life is to continue as they are but to get rid of the unpleasant complications. They view their situation as normal. For them their lives are normal, since alcoholism permits a masquerade of normalcy, even if it isn't what the nonalcoholic world understands normalcy to be.

The critical time for alcoholics comes when they are not able to meet life's problems, even in their own world of fantasy and with their own wobbling philosophy. Then they must settle for something less than the role in which they have imagined themselves. They rationalize that this acceptance of a lesser role in society and in their own circle can be nullified by a studious application of serious thought to their drinking. Their resentments yield temporarily to the effect of this new drinking plan, giving them grandiose notions of their own worth and merit, thus reinforcing their original concept of an alcoholic normalcy.

Sometimes alcoholics become captives of an overpowering dread of ever again accepting the mature responsibilities of a truly normal life. No matter how strenuously they may insist that their capabilities can be put to the test of self-reliance, they postpone taking action as long as possible, giving one excuse or another for evading the crucial decision to face a life without liquor.

No evasion is too low or improbable for an alcoholic hard pressed to come to a decision. One man, a strapping durable type, studied medical books to learn the symptoms of angina. He sought out a doctor, went through a review of his symptoms, and after several visits during which he studiously avoided being given an electrocardiogram bamboozled the doctor into prescribing an ounce of brandy once a day in addition to other medication. And so, brandishing the doctor's order, he went on a binge that would have stopped the heart of a dinosaur. When he was finally placed under treatment the electrocardiogram taken to determine whether he could take one of the chemical "fences" used to inhibit the use of alcohol showed that his heart was normal.

Others procrastinate on promises they make to relatives to undergo treatment. They will do it tomorrow, or next Monday, or after Christmas and New Year.

Examined with an unprejudiced eye, the rationalizations and evasions of the alcoholic are not greatly different from those of the nonalcoholic except in harmful degree. Social drinkers do not forsake the rewarding use of alcohol without a very powerful motive and considerable soul-searching. They are suspicious of people who do not drink with them, and they detect a threat to their enjoyment in the very presence of a nondrinker at their social functions.

What is most puzzling about the disease is the role of alcohol in causing alcoholism. Certain conditions, internally and externally, have to exist to create a vulnerability to alcohol. The body becomes increasingly unable to metabolize alcohol. The environmental conditions are right for the individual's acceptance of alcohol as a problem solver. The neurological conditions have to show a particular profile. And slowly, by easy stages, the individual enters into the lonely land of fancy to search among its broken dreams for the fellowship, happiness, and hope without which man is nothing.

To face a life without liquor alcoholics must be coached to use the abilities and positive assets remaining to them to overcome the inertia and passive acceptance of their sorry situation. Their assets and talents must be unearthed, identified, evaluated. They must then be convinced that these assets and abilities will provide building blocks for new, durable, reinforced lives without addiction to liquor.

The process of unearthing such useful building materials is sometimes complicated by their feelings of guilt and worthlessness. There is infinite pathos in the dilemma of a sick person who feels that his sickness is a disgrace. All the precepts from well-meant advice will not alter this condition until the alcoholic understands the nature of the illness.

There is a standard definition of alcoholism in wide use, which says much the same thing that other definitions say about the environmental, psychological, physiological, and economic etiology of alcoholism. It was compiled by the World Health Organization. "Alcoholism is any form of drinking which in its extent goes beyond the traditional and customary 'dietary' use, or the ordinary compliance with the social drinking customs of the whole community concerned, irrespective of the etiological factors leading to such behavior and irrespective also of the extent to which such etiological factors are dependent upon heredity, constitution, or acquired physiopathological and metabolic influences."

It will be seen that it may be meaningful to the professional, but it is not much use to the layman who may be inclined to read into its loose provisions things that are not intended to be there.

Three Faces of Hal

The crisis that provides the dramatic climax in drinking behavior when, for the first time, an alcoholic recognizes that his drinking is out of control, is not always so acute that one is unmistakably in need of help. Often the need for help is expressed in *almost normal* ways with a kind of unquiet, or failure to achieve ease. In the best sense of the word *disease* describes the condition.

The case of Hal is typical of a great many problem drinkers who are concealed by the protective coloring of the drinking culture of our time—the universal socializing over cocktails, the business conference over drinks, the social functions which almost always include opportunities to drink, whether it be a formal dance or a casual, neighborly visit.

Hal asked for help without prompting from any specific person among his friends, associates, and family. He had seen my name in a newspaper article on alcoholism and had decided to inquire of his own volition.

"Please understand," he said, "I don't think I am an alcoholic. But strange things happen to me when I am drinking that never happened before. Maybe I should see a psychiatrist. . . ." His voice trailed off. "No, let's face it," he went on with a new briskness. "I want the bad news if it is bad news. I want an opinion, not from a doctor, not from A.A. and not from people who used to drink with me.

"I'm just not clicking," Hal went on, an elaborately casual attitude began to take shape. He crossed his legs, tapped a cigarette meticulously on the ash tray, changed his anxious tone to one of a lighter, almost bantering mood.

"You know how it is when you tell a joke that everyone has heard before, when it falls like a lead balloon and everyone laughs politely but not heartily. Well when I am drinking anywhere around my boss, my associates or even my family, I get the impression that I'm not clicking, they aren't with me, they are *observing* me. I felt for a while that they thought that I was about to blow my top, but I know that it isn't so much that as just not clicking, and the only thing I can find to account for it is the drinking.

"How have you been drinking? Not when, but how?"

Hal grinned. "Steadily," he said.

"Have you had any blackouts?"

"Pulled a blank? Sure, three or four times. But don't get me wrong. I can drink most of my crowd under the table. They don't mess around drinking with Hal, because they know it's Hal who closes the bar."

"Do you think that your system has developed greater tolerance for alcohol?"

"I guess I've got a system like a sponge," said Hal.

"Then what's bothering you?" I asked.

"What's bothering me is that I don't quit when others quit. I just keep going."

"What else have you done that bothers you?"

"Well, you may not appreciate this, being a woman. I bought two suits yesterday with the money my wife expected to use to redecorate the living room, and I don't know why I did it. I haven't told her yet, but when I do— zowie! We'll be off on another fight."

"Anything else?"

"Yes, I don't like the way the boss questions my progress reports when I complete a job and stuff like that. I'm sent out from the plant to install machinery and check it out —on the road sort of."

"Why do you think your boss suspects something wrong?"

"Well, if I drink during working hours I have to pad the reports a little to account for time. . . . He knows how it is. He was a troubleshooter once himself."

I did not take any notes while he was talking. But it was timely to ask questions about his personal background, name, age, residence, and so forth, while he was communicative.

"Wait a minute," he said. "All I want is to find out if I'm in trouble with the stuff and what to do to slow down a little."

"I have to know something about you," I told him. "I'm not just curious. Whatever you tell me is confidential and it will all be of help."

"Do you think I'm an alcoholic?"

"I'm not going to answer that. You can answer that for yourself after you find out a little bit more about alcoholism and alcohol."

"I know about alcohol. I've drunk enough of it."

"Do you know how your body utilizes alcohol?"

"Oh, boy! Do I know. . . ."

"No, seriously, do you know anything about the way your body metabolizes alcohol, or do you just know what the effect is as your body uses it?"

"O.K. You're the doctor."

"No, I'm not the doctor. I'm just the counselor. I'm not even sure you need a doctor, but I am sure that you ought to get some accurate information about alcohol and alcoholism, and about the behavior patterns that develop in alcoholism. *Then* we can talk about whether or not you are an alcoholic. At least you have an advantage over many who suffer from alcoholism. You have asked for information. Now, will you tell me something about you?"

"My name's Harold———and I'm 39 years old. I'm married, I've two kids, and I live in a twenty-thousand-dollar

house at———with a fifteen-thousand-dollar mortgage.
What else?"

I jotted down some notes as he talked. His history was
(again that phrase) almost normal.

But, there were certain discords in his family relations.
He had been churchgoing as a youth, attending not only
regular church services, but also choir rehearsals, youth activities, and Bible classes. Was this his own idea or was it
something that his family had required of him?

"Well, it was mostly the family. That's the way they
lived. Church was their social life while they lived together.
And I went along with it until I finally cut out. I don't think
I've been inside a church a half dozen times since."

He had started drinking while in technical school after
his first year of apprenticeship as a tool maker.

"What kind of drinking?"

"Oh, you know, *drinking*. Chug-a-lug. How many beers
can you hold and can you drink a can in one continuous
swallow? Kid stuff!"

"Did you feel guilty about starting to drink while you
were away from home?"

"Guilty? I don't know. I guess I knew that my mother
took a dim view of drinking. She never had anything in the
house. No drinking. No dancing. No card playing."

"When you went home after technical school how did
you feel about the drinking?"

"I suppose I didn't feel as close to my mother. I didn't
fit in. It all seemed kind of dull at home, at least compared
to the freedom of living away from home."

"What about drinking and dating while you were a teen-
ager?"

"Oh, the usual. As a matter of fact I met my wife on a
blind date arranged by a schoolmate and we hit it off right
away."

"Hit it off, how?"

"Oh, she liked the things I liked and we had something to talk about. She wanted to get away from home she said because her mother tried to run her life. Anyway, we were married the summer after I graduated and held my first job."

"Are you still interested in the same things?"

He laughed. "You mean drinking? No, she doesn't drink. I guess she didn't want to get away from her mother as much as she said. I have a little mother-in-law trouble. Too much mama at times and I blow my stack. You know how it is."

"Does your mother-in-law interfere?"

"Don't they all?"

"No, not all. What seems to be the trouble?"

"Oh, no trouble. If I'm away on the road installing, or out a couple of nights on the job, she takes the kids home to mother, and then there's the long face. . . . Anyway, what does this have to do with drinking? I don't like to have mama served to me four times a day."

"Let's get back to what we were talking about—help for you. That is much more important. You are the important one in this problem."

He sat back relaxed and exhaled a long, pent-up breath.

"I believe you are serious about wanting help. I believe you can do it. What would you like to do about it? How can I be of help? Can we work out a plan of action together—you and your wife and me? I trust you and you can trust me."

"You have heard all this guff before," said Hal. I shouldn't bother you with my troubles."

"It's not a bother. This is my job. This office exists to help people with their problems. It has been here a long time. We have more work each year, not less. Yes, I've heard a lot of 'guff,' as you put it, but I've heard a lot that isn't guff too. I've heard enough of both to know the difference. And I have learned that it is better to talk about it than to let it corrode inside. At least when it is put into words, we can examine it and throw out what we can't use. Do you agree?"

"That's been my trouble. I can't tell the difference any more."

"Well, let's guff awhile, and see what we have left to work with." At this Hal smiled.

"What are you willing to do to help yourself? I'll stand by as a friend might. Anything you do to help yourself belongs entirely to you. I'm just the helper. You're the leader. You have already taken the lead by coming in for assistance."

"Well, I hadn't thought of it like that." Hal's face paled a bit. His facial muscles quivered, then firmed. He squared his shoulders and straightened his head. His eyes brightened. The flow of words no longer hesitated. We had discovered some missing link and the discovery had sparked a more positive attitude.

"I've been letting this stuff get me down for a long time," he said. "I haven't had it out of my system long enough to find out where or how I missed the boat. It was easier to drink and go my way than to try to help Elsa find something to interest her while I was at work. Marriage changed things for her too. And I can see now that she went back to her mother as she always did, since she didn't get any help from me. I always had my work and she didn't want to go to the ball games or hockey games with me at night, so I just went out anyway, caught a couple of drinks down the street, and went to the games alone. This was all right for a while, but then she started to nag, trying to get me to go to a movie with her. I never liked the movies, especially the kind she wanted to see. The love-sick kind.

"We've both let things go too far. Her mother likes to have her come home. But now the old lady is telling her that I'm no good for her. She doesn't say it in so many words. She just tells Elsa she could have done better if she had waited a while longer to get married, instead of running away with the first man who came along. This upsets Elsa too and she doesn't know what to believe.

"I think I have an idea now how we can start again. I love her even if she can't see baseball and hockey. We ought to be able to work it out somehow. I don't know yet how we can handle her mother. She's a strong woman and has a way of making Elsa feel guilty. Just how to get her mother out of the way won't be easy—maybe she'll help me."

"First things first. It will not be easy to abstain from drinking for the next few weeks either. I'm sure you can do it, but I hope you won't try to do it alone. There will be times when unexpected things go wrong, at work or at home. Elsa may not agree with you on some point of change. She may not see it your way and it may be difficult to keep your composure with her. You said she too was beginning to get mixed up about whether her mother was right or not. This is the time you mentioned when you walked out on her and took a drink. It could happen again. Will you call me instead of taking a drink if this should happen? Sometimes just a telephone call to talk about it will break up the tension."

"Sure, I'll call you first."

"Elsa left her mother in the first place to marry you. Are you willing to have her come in to see me?"

Hal frowned slightly as he said, "Well now, she'll tell you a lot of things about me that aren't pretty. Some are just her ideas and not as bad as they sound—things about how my drinking is hurting the kids."

"Can you let me be the judge of what she says? I don't know any angels."

"It might work . . . you've heard that kind of stuff before. Oh sure, I'll ask her to come in to see you."

"Will you ask her to telephone me and we can make an appointment that will be convenient for both of us."

Hal relaxed again. This got him off the hook. "Yes, I guess that would be better." He became friendly again. He was not alone. He had a friend for himself and his wife. Someone to guide them both if they started to take a bypass.

Suddenly his manners returned and he became objective. "I've taken up a lot of your time," he said as he rose from his chair with outstretched hand. "Thanks, I'm glad I came to see you. You will hear from my wife soon. Maybe my mother will come with her. I'll have to feel her out. It won't be more than a day or two. Thanks again."

He walked firmly to the door, smiled, and left. We were on our way.

But when Hal's mother and his wife appeared to discuss Hal's situation, it was as if I had never met the man they described.

To the fond eyes of women the erosion of the character of their men by alcohol is usually as stark as the black clouds of a gathering storm. These two women, anxious to get help for the same man, one for a son and the other for a husband, illustrate how their concern casts a different light upon two different faces of one individual's character. I had seen the public Hal, now I met the intimate, personal, family Hal.

Elsa had a quiet, somber face, white waxen skin, dark ringleted hair, and large, soft brown eyes—eyes that seemed to plead and convey a feeling of helplessness, or at the very least, soft compliance.

Hal's mother was one of those energetic, small women, whose no nonsense air frequently covers a deep insecurity. The mother came to the interview directly from her office job. The wife had left her children in the care of her *mother*, and had agreed to meet her mother-in-law and join her in discussing help for her husband.

"How does he drink?"

The young wife made a slight grimace of distaste. "He drinks until he falls down on the floor," she said. "This frightens me and you know I have a baby. I don't think he *has* to drink that way. When he visits my folks with me he has a beer or two and that is all. But when he gets home to our house he drinks until he falls down in a stupor. I have had to leave him on the floor. I mean that he was too heavy for me to lift. I don't do that any more—I have left him. This is the second time and this time I mean it. No more soft-soaping me. I won't go back unless he does something about his drinking, unless he proves that he wants to stop."

Hal's mother listened silently to this, nodding her head faintly in agreement, shaking her head in pain when the wife told how her son fell down on the floor and slept there drunk.

"What can we do?" both women asked. "Something has got to be done right away. Does he really mean what he says about trying to get help?"

"Very little is going to be done right away," I said. "This hasn't happened to him overnight. It has been years— probably since boyhood."

The mother twisted her hands and covered her third finger on her left hand. But I had already noticed that she wore no wedding ring.

"I'm divorced," she said lamely. "Years ago, when Hal was a boy."

The wife turned her large brown eyes toward her mother-in-law, her lips parted as if she were hearing of this for the first time.

"He was not quite eleven when I divorced my husband. I used to think that I divorced my husband because my son wanted me to. But I guess it wasn't that. My husband was very interested in cultural things—history, the arts, music, theatre—and I wasn't so much interested. He tried to interest me and he tried to explain things to my son, but my son was too small, too young to understand. Once he threatened to run away if I didn't divorce his father.

"I knew at last that we were not suited to one another. Hal was happy when I filed suit for divorce, but when I told him that my divorce was final he sobbed as if his heart would break. He told me that in spite of all his threats to run away he admired his father's intelligence, his efforts to better himself. He seemed to remember and would always bring up the fact that it was he who had insisted I get a divorce."

The wife stared hard at her mother-in-law, waiting for a chance to say something. "I won't go back to him," she said. "I am not going to ask him to come back to me, not until he does what he says he wants to do about drinking. I want a home of my own, not a place filled with unhappiness and fear. I want him sober, and if he doesn't do this I won't take him back."

Hal hadn't mentioned that his wife had threatened to leave him.

"I'm glad you have made a decision about it," I said. "If you threaten to leave him if he doesn't stop drinking, and he has always wheedled you into taking him back, you must be firm and unshakable when you finally walk out. Otherwise he won't have any reason to believe that he can't soft-soap you again."

"Yes," the mother said. "She is right, much as I hate to say so. I lost patience with him. I wanted him so much to succeed. He had to leave high school in his third year to go to work, but he did very well. He went to a technical school and learned to be a toolmaker. He really has done this by himself."

"Some weeks he earned two hundred dollars," the wife said, as if corroboration of his earning capacity was necessary to properly evaluate his talents.

But the mother went on. She didn't hear anything but her own voice, nagging at her son. Why don't you do this? Why don't you go to church any more? Why don't you do that? "I was always at him. I know I was being emotional. I hoped that when he got married it would make a man of him. He was very attractive, wasn't he? He still is attractive. I didn't want him to be a toolmaker all his life. That's the way his father was. His father just wanted to be a sign painter if he couldn't be an artist. So I have always been after Hal. He would come home to me when Elsa left him, like after this last big blowup. He wanted sympathy, but I don't think he should be given sympathy for not taking care of his wife and children. It's all too much for both of us, isn't it dear."

The wife nodded. "It's too much the way it is, but I have made up my mind not to give in this time. My mother says that I have to make the decision. I've made it. Now it's up to him. But I understand that he can't make a choice of what to do. Something went wrong with his life before I ever met him, before we were married."

"Yes," his mother said. "Something happened to him."

"Will you tell him that I would like to talk to him?" I asked Hal's mother.

"He won't come near me when he's drinking."

"He will get in touch with you or his wife sooner or later," I said. "And remember he came here of his own volition. He will come again."

It wasn't surprising that Hal had started drinking soon after he first sought help. This happens to many alcoholics who are at the point of making a decision to give up drinking. The thought that they will have to cope with their anxieties, frustrations, tensions, and physical distress without the help of liquor is overwhelming or the effort seems to them too formidable.

"How soon after he asked you to come to see me did he start drinking again?"

"Immediately after and that's why we didn't come right away. We thought it was just one of his stories, but we found that booklet that you gave him and decided to come."

"I would like to have him know that he can come here and talk things over, and that drinking hasn't anything to do with how I feel about it. Alcoholics drink. I have to expect that."

"I'll find him and tell him," Hal's wife said. "I will do that much for him."

It was two weeks before I talked to Hal. Between the time his wife and mother talked to me and the time he appeared again to ask for help he had been in the hospital and had been through severe withdrawal. He was suspended from his job and the bills he hadn't paid had closed in.

This time there was no pretense, no effort to put a brighter aspect to the dark facts.

"What am I going to do?" Hal groaned. "What can I do? The bank says it is going to foreclose on the house. The installment house has grabbed the refrigerator and the washing machine. The next thing to go is the car—three months behind in payments. And God I feel sick. What's the use?"

"Take one thing at a time. Do you really want to try to stay sober?"

"Yes, I want to try. But how can I with the roof falling in on me? I'm my father all over again."

"I don't know your father so I won't answer that. But I doubt it. Do you want to get your job back?"

"Sure I do."

"Give me your boss's name and telephone number."

"Wait a minute. You're not going to talk to him and tell him about this?"

"Why not? Do you think he doesn't know, Hal? Seriously, do you think he doesn't know?"

"That's all he will need to find out—that you think I'm an alcoholic. Then—kaput!"

"What's the real situation? Are you suspended or fired?"

"Well, the same as fired."

"Then, if you haven't got the job what's the harm in talking to your boss? Maybe he will change his mind."

"O.K.," Hal agreed. "What do you want me to do besides that?"

"There's a doctor I want you to see—a psychiatrist."

"You mean you think I'm nuts?"

"No, I mean that I want you to tell the doctor very frankly about yourself and your drinking. Don't worry about paying for this first visit. I will ask him to bill you when you are on your feet again. Right now I want you to be honest and cooperative with the doctor. He can help you to understand some of the emotional problems you have been through. You can trust him. And you can trust me."

When Hal left me to keep the appointment with the doctor he was as dejected as a mortal can be just this side of despair.

"Call me on the telephone after you see the doctor," I said. "And good luck!"

"I need it," said Hal. "I need it."

Hal's boss—the head of the factory service department listened thoughtfully as I explained who I was and the reason for the call. He had a pleasant soft Scottish burr and a slow, careful manner of speaking.

"He's not fired," Hal's boss said. "I sent him home to keep him out of trouble. He's one of my good men. He has a way with cranky machinery that we need very much. But he can't go on drinking the way he does because the people over me won't put up with it. If he can come back and work steady everything will be all right and nobody upstairs will be any the wiser."

"Do you have a plant doctor?"

"Yes, there's a medical department."

"Have you thought about talking Hal's situation over with them? He needs treatment, and if he's kept on the job while he's under treatment someone will have to know about the possibilities of relapse as he makes progress toward recovery."

The boss was silent for a moment. "I understand what you mean," he said. "Let me talk with the plant doctor. I'll let you know what he says."

The plant physician, it developed, was interested in a professional opinion on Hal's case and wanted to know more about the contemplated treatment and exchange medical information concerning the treatment.

"You'll be hearing from our doctor. He wants to talk to the doctor you sent Hal to," the boss explained. "But, I guess it's settled. We can put Hal back to work as soon as he's able."

Step by step the pieces of Hal's disordered life were being nudged back into place. There was still Elsa, the bills, the unknown thing from the past that gnawed at Hal's composure and drove him to the only tranquillizer he knew. We had taken only the preliminary action and motivated Hal to do something about his alcoholism. The painstaking job of counseling was yet to follow.

Hal's situation was in no way unusual for an alcoholic, but the fact that he had taken the first step toward recovery and initiative in seeking help without any pressure from his family or his employer made his quest for recovery unusually promising.

By far the greater number of alcoholics who accept help and treatment for alcoholism do so because of a crisis that paralyzes their own initiative. The alcoholics who seek help without motivation from others are much rarer than the majority who respond to the prompting and initiative of relatives and friends. The self-referred alcoholic is self-referred only in name, and usually claims it was his own idea out of pride. Most therapists are content to leave it that way because alcoholics must take responsibility for themselves and their striving for sobriety in order to gain confidence in complete recovery.

But, what is of greater significance in Hal's story is what might be called the three faces of Hal—his view of himself and his drinking pattern, his wife's view of Hal and his drinking, and his mother's view of her son for whom she had such driving ambition. Here you can observe the interplay of forces that raked the sensibilities of Hal and contributed to his alcoholism and his maladjustment in a life that should have been happy and contented.

CHAPTER FOUR

Lisa—An Alcoholic Memoir

Lisa first contacted me by phone. Women alcoholics seeking help usually make a telephone approach. "Is this Mrs. Whitney?" And then, "I have a call for you, hold on please. Here's your party."

"Hello, this is Mrs. Whitney speaking."

Silence, and then a faint sound of breathing. Behind the breathing sound, almost like counterpoint, I could hear the last few bars of "Stardust," and then an announcer's voice saying, "You are listening to WNAC, 680 on your dial."

Once again, "This is Mrs. Whitney speaking. Are you calling me?"

The sound of breathing, and then the faint click as whoever was on the other end hung up.

This was repeated three times that day. The operator would complete the call, there would be the sound of breathing and the muffled sound of a radio playing, and then the click as the connection was broken.

There were several things about the phone calls that told a great deal. The calls had been put through by an operator who had been instructed to get me on the line. There was a person on the other end with the telephone close enough to pick up the sound of breathing. And there was a radio playing in the background. It was a local station so it was someone within the metropolitan area. Someone wanted to talk and hadn't quite summoned up enough courage to go through with the plan. Sooner or later the mysterious calls would be explained.

Within two days there was an explanation. Another call came through with the same sequence—the sound of

50

breathing, the radio in the background. And so I said, "I can't hear the radio very clearly. Will you move the telephone closer to it?"

The radio volume rose. There was no click of the instrument being hung up.

"Why don't you talk to me about whatever it is that's bothering you?" I said.

There was a silence, more breathing sounds, and then a woman's voice, words slurred, frosted with tears, "I am sorry that I have bothered you. I shouldn't have bothered you. I shouldn't have done it. I just wanted to hear a voice. The operators in the hotel won't talk to me any more. I'm sorry. Goodbye."

"Wait a moment," I said, hastily. "You can call me anytime or come and see me. I know you must be lonely."

That was the first groping for help. The nameless voice was identified weeks later when a woman of fifty-five or so came to see me.

"Can you help me?" she said. "My daughter was missing for over a week and we finally found her in a hotel room. She had used the telephone but the only outside calls she made were to your office."

Her small shaking hand dug in her purse as she spoke; withdrawing a handful of white slips of paper, slips from a hotel switchboard, which she pushed across my desk, then sat back in her chair silent, as though she expected me to take over from there.

"I hope I can be of help," I said, gently. "I remember several mysterious telephone calls from a woman who did not give her name. I had an idea that the calls would be explained. Let me ask—is it a drinking problem, and are you afraid of the truth?"

"No, I've known for some time that my daughter was drinking far too much, but she would never discuss it with me. We see less and less of her since she moved into an apartment about a year ago. She was very sick when we found her. . . . She's home with us now, recuperating, but she'll be leaving again soon. She works for a decorating firm, and she travels to New York frequently. Isn't there something we can do?"

"Perhaps we can figure something out, but I will have to know more about your daughter. Do you think she will accept help now?"

"She admitted she was desperate when we brought her home. She seemed like a frightened child."

"What was she like before she left home?"

"She was a very quiet little girl," the mother began, "rather old-fashioned and prim. She was plain, not beautiful. She was sweet and sort of shy. I always remember her like that. But today she's a stranger, someone I don't know. It is almost as if she weren't my own child but someone who took the place of my own child. She doesn't act like anyone in my family, or anyone in my husband's family, that I know of."

"How old is she?"

"She's just turned 34. Last week was her birthday."

"Is she married, or has she ever been married?"

"No, she hasn't ever been serious with a man. She's had a few beaus, but nothing serious."

"Are you ready to do anything that has to be done for your daughter?"

"I'm at my wits' end. Her father and I will do anything we can. This is the first time she has disappeared this way. She always telephoned us when she went to New York in connection with her job. This time she didn't go, and when we got no response when we called her apartment and she didn't call us, we were frantic. A girl friend of hers gave us a clue as to where we might find her."

"I think it will be better if she talks with me before we discuss her further. Do you think that she will make an appointment to see me and talk about her problem?"

"I hope she will. I never can tell what she will do. Should I tell her that I have been to see you?"

"Yes, tell her the truth. Don't try to hide anything from her. Tell her how you located me. And assure her that whatever she does is entirely up to her."

The anxious mother agreed. Yet it was several days before I received a telephone call.

"This is Lisa————, L-I-S-A. Mother went to the movies. I would like to talk to you if I may. I think you sent a message by my mother that you would like to talk to me."

It was the voice of the mystery caller—clearer, less fuzzy. She would be able to come to see me after office hours.

When she appeared she turned out to be less plain than I had expected. She knew what to wear to emphasize her coloring and her features. Her clothes weren't expensive but were in good taste. She put her handbag on my desk and it gave a little clink. I smiled.

"You know what's in it, don't you?" she said.

I nodded. "Shall we talk over a cup of coffee?"

"I'd like that," she said.

As she talked about herself a definite profile of her personality and behavior emerged. It was like matching her silhouette against the dark outlines of other women who had been through a cruel experience with alcohol. The profiles ran together—similar, but utterly different.

The career that didn't yield its hoped for liberation from parental or family domination reminded me of many women alcoholics who also had overprotective mothers. I would talk to her sometime about them and about what they did to achieve recovery.

"I am desperately ashamed of the way I have been drinking," she told me. "I buy my liquor in half pints. It's easy to hide them. I can carry one in a handbag, and smuggle it in when I visit mother. I can slip it under the pillow

and drink it by myself. I tell the family that I'm going to bed
because I'm exhausted. You know how it makes me feel? I
feel the glow, the wonderful blossoming of dreams of things
I have always wanted and never could have. I can forget
that there will be a tomorrow when I will be ashamed of my
thoughts and my actions."

Yes, she was like another woman alcoholic in my experience, but she would be repelled to know about how Sally
drank. I could see Sally in silhouette, too, her needs no
different from those of this crushed woman. Sally was tall
and dark and wore her hair in the same kind of bun at the
nape of her neck. She had the same alternate humility and
wild anger. She had graduated with honors in English literature, but to earn a living for herself and for her dependent
father and mother she had taken a factory job. She couldn't
invite male friends to her home because her parents criti-
cized each visitor. She couldn't have much of a social life
outside of her deadly routine of bed and work because no
opportunities presented themselves to escape for even a few
hours the responsibility of her ailing parents. Sally couldn't
even smuggle a half pint of whisky into her home. She
would stop at the liquor store on her way home from work.
And she would pause in secluded doorways or vestibules as
she walked home from work and drink the half pint. Once or
twice she had passed out on the street before she reached
her home and the police picked her up. "I'm 38," she said,
"and I'm never going to be married, never going to find a
man who loves me. I'm tied to two old people until they die
and they aren't going to let me off the hook because I'm the
only child left at home."

But Sally mastered her problem and she finally married
happily because she learned that there was a way out of her
dilemma, that social agencies existed to help her care for
elderly and ailing parents. She learned to substitute reality
for escaping dreams of youth.

And so I said to Lisa, "Would you be interested to learn that other women have had drinking problems as serious as yours and yet have managed to get well?"

"I am not other women. I am me. You should know more about my mother and my father. They didn't tell you how they pry into my private affairs. They didn't tell you that I have a job that I like. They didn't tell you that every time I mention a man they immediately are planning a wedding.

"If I go out of town on business I have to telephone twice a day to let them know that I am not drinking. Whenever I get back and drop by to see them they go through all kinds of maneuvers to smell my breath.

"They try to tell me what's best for me. Bridge, clubs, lectures, things like that. It all bores me. I hate bridge. I can't stand women bickering and gossiping all evening. So I go to the movies. That's what I tell them. Or I creep into my apartment with a bottle. Sometimes I go to a hotel bar or a respectable cocktail lounge, hoping that someone I may meet there can help me change it all. But I never pick anyone up. I'm too shy for that, too conscious of keeping up appearances."

She went on and on, obviously relieved to talk about her situation, to put into words her resentment of her mother's overprotectiveness. And I let her run on until at last she fell silent and sat staring into my face as if she were looking through me at some future time that was drearier, if possible, than her present.

"Now," I said, "I hope you are all through beating yourself in the face. Is there someone in your family who understands you?"

"I'm stuck with Mother. . . . Oh, I shouldn't say things about Mother. I know she really can't help being the way she is. But dear God when is she going to stop trying to train me like a poor little tree being made to grow against a wall?"

"Have you ever talked to her about why you drink?"

"Yes, I've tried, but she always says she knows best and she will help me arrange my life."

"Do you think she will understand if someone else talks to her, someone whose opinion she might respect?"

"I don't know. What could she possibly be told that would help me now?"

"Well, she could be told exactly how you feel, that you don't want to drink, but that her interferences in your personal life are a part of your problem. She's probably not aware that in order for you to control your drinking you have to make your own decisions and have to manage your own personal life. Right now you talk as if you are defeated before you make any effort at all. But it comes right down to what you do to help yourself. And you will learn more about that as you go along. It isn't going to be easy. The only thing I ask of you is whether you want to try. If you do, then we will try together to work out a plan for you to live without liquor."

"Do you think they will let me do it?"

"They love you. They are concerned about you. They want you to find yourself. But they are no different from the majority of people. They do not understand your illness. They aren't even convinced it is an illness."

"When do I start?"

"Now."

"What about this in my handbag?"

"What about it? That's your first decision."

One needs a closer look at Lisa. Her name was a testimonial to her Pilgrim ancestry—one of those direct lines of descent that make genealogical charts so unassailable for those who overvalue an ancient and honorable name.

Lisa—Melissa—was in the middle phases of alcoholism by the time she was thirty-one, but she had disguised her distress so well that only a very few people were aware that she drank, much less that she drank compulsively.

Now and again you would see a photograph of her serving on a committee for some good work, or there would be reference to the fact that she had won recognition as a highly trained and skillful interior decorator. She had to have a job to support herself because there wasn't much left of the family name and money.

And so Lisa—slender, rather patrician looking, quietly dressed in clothes of good quality and taste—went her own way getting drunk in a ladylike fashion. Sometimes she would retire unnoticed to a hotel or motel, later to an apartment of her own, to continue drinking until the distress of her inadequacy, anxiety, and tension were anaesthetized. She was always able to account for her absences from home with carefully contrived falsehoods which in the end contributed to her feelings of guilt and unworthiness.

She had carefully schooled herself in attitudes and behavior, living an inner life that cut her off from stark reality. There were many little mannerisms one might notice, such as the way she held her head when she was talking directly to someone facing her. She would turn slightly to the left and gaze at her auditor obliquely, eyelids narrowed and her head held high, so that she appeared to be looking down upon whomever she addressed. This was her way of concealing the fact that vision in her left eye was very weak, and it was more noticeable when she was tired. Without glasses, and now without liquor, the world was a complete blur to her.

The inadequacies that had crippled her as a person were layer by layer a concealment of the fact—in no way remarkable—that she had been born with weak eyesight and that she had a foolish mother who believed that girls who wore glasses were somehow not attractive to men and that corrective glasses would in some way make her daughter an unsuitable match for a socially acceptable husband. She was a silent partner in Lisa's deceptive cunning.

Lisa had been through a girlhood of incessant hand-wringing by her overprotective mother over the tragedy of her having weak eyes. The fact that she had not married by the time she was thirty-one was constantly bewailed by a now aging mother, which didn't help Lisa to accept her defective vision.

After our first meeting, there was a second appointment scheduled. But even as the appointment was made I had a distinct feeling that Lisa wouldn't keep it; and she didn't. Instead, she telephoned that an important professional meeting had come up.

Twelve months of silence followed. There was one telephone call from Lisa's mother during which she asked several tentative questions that were plainly directed to finding out whether or not I had talked to her daughter. But when I made it plain that I had talked to her daughter only once and that I preferred not to discuss the problem over the telephone, her mother hung up.

One summer day Lisa telephoned. She identified herself, using Melissa, her full name, to explain who she was and why she called asking for an appointment. This imperious demanding attitude is familiar to all who counsel or treat alcoholics. Many people suffering from this disease conjure ideas of grandeur that apply only to their own convenience. They are finger snappers who cannot tolerate delay once they decide that they want something. Otherwise their ideas will be lost and they will feel the pangs of failure and despondency—not wanted, out of things—thus they cut themselves off from normal society.

Lisa had dressed very carefully for her appointment. Her hair was beautifully arranged. Her nails were manicured and delicately polished. She held her head high and gave me that curious oblique look. "I really do not know why I am here," she explained. "Oh, a long time ago a lady doctor, a psychologist you know, practically a member of the family, suggested I see you. She is away now on some sort of an expedition, but I thought I would drop in for a chat while I could take an hour or two off from my job."

Lisa ignored the fact that I had talked to her a year previously. We chatted pleasantly enough trying to establish some sort of rapport, but she was very sensitive to any reference to drinking, or to any specific discussion of treatment for alcoholism.

"I think I should tell you that I have been in psychiatry once or twice, but I'm not particularly impressed with what the psychiatrist did for me. I find that a heart to heart talk with a great stone image is probably as useful."

Like so many others Lisa was projecting a lack of confidence and a great skepticism of the usefulness of any discussion with her about the basic problem underlying her compulsive drinking, without saying flatly, "I do not agree with anything that you say and I don't think you can do anything for me." A roundabout way of saying "I don't know who I am, where I am going, how to see the right road for me, or how to find incentive to make a positive decision for myself or future."

If I called her first impression of me anything other than unpleasant I would be stretching a point. But, she revealed a great deal about herself during the verbal skirmishing. After talking with her for an hour, I was certain about two things. Either she did not now have a job or had been suspended from the one she had, and she had had trouble with the police. She had lied to me at first about what had brought about the visit after the lapse of a year.

Finally she admitted the facts. She had been arrested for driving her automobile while drunk and she had been suspended from her job, pending a conference with the firm's manager.

When Lisa was leaving I gave her some booklets to read about alcoholism, about the motivation to undergo treatment and about the public attitudes toward alcoholism and alcoholics.

A day or two later I received a courteous note from Lisa at my home, not at the office. She explained she had obtained my home address from a friend of mine.

"I am doubtful about my course of events," she wrote. "But, I *am* doing some serious thinking. I feel that now I will try myself to see what I can do to remedy this situation, but I will keep you informed whatever happens. I have read the booklets and they are most interesting. Many thanks."

One needs to understand her reasons for favoring me with knowledge of events that might involve her if she failed on her own. She needed help—she might just as well have said, "Please, don't forget me. You will hear from me again.

Her having gone to the trouble of writing a thank-you note and making a social contact, directing the note to my home, indicated a great deal. She did not want to associate herself with a formal resource devoted to alcoholism, but she wanted the benefits. She didn't want to lose contact, but rather than humble herself in her own estimation to seek the kind of help that other alcoholics seek, she was going to try to avoid such suggestions as Alcoholics Anonymous, or treatment by a physician specializing in alcoholism. As I interpreted the maneuver, she felt that if she could avoid the painful admission that she was an alcoholic, transferring her dependency to a mother figure who had no authority over her, she could save her pride and continue to feel that she could run her own affairs.

She telephoned to me one night, obviously after she had been drinking, and chirped brightly, "Do you have any suggestions for Lisa? Lisa's feeling lousy. Say, that almost scans like a jingle. Lisa's feeling lousy."

"Would you like to go to a meeting of A.A.? Just sit in and listen quietly and see what goes on there?"

"You've got to be kidding. I told you my opinion of A.A.? If I didn't, brace yourself. I will."

"It really isn't going to make any difference, Lisa. It was just a suggestion. There are other things available."

"There," Lisa said, "I've hurt your feelings. Let me explain my reaction to A.A. There was this fellow—a very nice man really—who didn't approve of my drinking. And one night he took me to an A.A. meeting, sort of as if it was a kind of slumming expedition. I sat there and I listened to all those characters. They were telling drunk stories—their own—and the stories were pretty dull. A more unimaginative bunch of drunks I have never seen. Personally, I could have told them some dandy anecdotes. Like the time I went swimming at the aquarium. But never mind. . . . What I wanted to say is that I haven't anything in common with A.A. people. Don't get me wrong, I'm no snob. But if I'm going to spend a lot of time with a group of people I at least want to be sure that we have something in common."

"Where was this meeting? Was it in your own community?"

"Of course not. It was over in Charlestown. Most of the men work on the docks and the women, the two or three who were there, had had it, if you know what I mean."

Lisa was rejecting A.A. because she had tried a single group—a group practising A.A. principles quite as sincerely as any other, but who actually were not an ideal choice for establishing a secure contact with Lisa, who, despite her denials, was an intellectual snob.

"Will you go to an A.A. meeting with me?" I asked.

"What have I got to lose except time? Where's the meeting?"

I made a swift check of the A.A. meeting list, chose one in an upper middle class suburb, held in the lounge of a private civic club. It was a so-called open meeting open to friends and relatives of alcoholics. There were two speakers left on the program when we arrived—a jolly, chubby house-wife and a tall, lean man who was a famous boatbuilder.

The jolly woman kept the audience chuckling with her account of juggling the household money to conceal her secret purchases of liquor. Lisa muttered behind her hand, "Laughing girl was an embezzler. I'm not impressed."

When the second speaker stood up Lisa drew in a quick gasp. "Let's get out right now. We know each other. He built a boat for my father. He sailed in one of the America's cup races—crew. Tell me—was this a put-up job?"

"As a matter of fact I chose this meeting at random, Lisa. You will learn that there are all kinds of people in A.A. —high status people and what you might call low status people. They tend to join people with whom they feel comfortable. There are such groups that are frankly snobbish and groups where the language would raise blisters on paint. But it's what the people get out of it, not the way they express themselves, that counts. Let's stay and hear what he has to say. He can't see you away down here in back."

"That's the way you feel about it," Lisa said. "Personally I'm not about to play bleeding heart and discuss my personal affairs with a group who seem to enjoy their misery."

"No one is asking you to discuss anything. You are here to listen."

The boatbuilder talked very quietly, softly, explaining the slow attrition of his skills as a yachtsman, designer, and boat builder; how his life and his youth had been worn away; how summer by summer, regatta by regatta, he had moved deeper and deeper into alcoholism, farther and farther off the safe and familiar soundings by which he charted his life.

Lisa sat with her fingers intertwined, almost wringing hands as she caught glimpses of hidden aspects in the life of one person whom she knew and whose involvement in alcoholism she had never suspected.

She observed the well-groomed women selling raffle tickets, serving coffee, chatting together, greeting friends. The boatbuilder walked past Lisa, nodded almost imperceptibly, but didn't speak to her.

"I think I will visit a few meetings," she said. "Just audit them, so to speak, and see what they have to offer."

"Do you want someone to go with you?"

"No. I'm a big girl. Give me a list of meetings, if you will, and I'll see if I can find my kind of people."

Two weeks went by and no word from Lisa, and then I received another letter at my home. "I now understand a great deal more, especially after listening, and some talking on my part. I want you to know that I do realize the seriousness of my situation if I continue to drink.

"I do want to talk with you some more. Is there any way in which I could meet you outside of your office? Could I come to your home on Saturday or Sunday. My work is such that it is difficult to see you during the week. I am not ready to talk about my problems with members of the group (A.A.) but if you can see me I would certainly appreciate it."

This note was a mixture of falsehood and fact. She was pretending that her job was secure. She had been set down for trial on the charge of driving while under the influence and had lost her automobile license temporarily, which explained her reference to the seriousness of her situation if she continued to drink. But Lisa wanted to talk to someone in whom she had confidence but who was not closely identified with her family or her friends, or even the A.A. group. She got her invitation to visit me at my home the following weekend.

The weekend was chosen for a particular reason. Lisa had, by many references to parties, cocktail hours, and so forth, indicated that her heaviest drinking was done between Friday night and Sunday. Because of her expressed desire to identify with professional persons I felt sure that she wouldn't come to see me while drunk and that in order to be sober when she arrived she would have to break up her drinking pattern.

Ten o'clock Saturday night, and Lisa had not put in an appearance. But, around midnight an automobile paused briefly at the driveway to my home, someone ran up the driveway, and there was a knock at the door. It was Lisa.

"I had dinner with a friend," she said, "and we talked a great deal. I had just one drink, and I'm proud of myself because I didn't want to come to see you fuzzy or anything like that. May I come in?"

Lisa had presented herself at the threshold of her personal crisis. I saw the carefully contrived façade of Lisa crumble and fall apart, revealing a badly frightened child—immature, self-pitying, capricious, and selfish—and this is what she saw of herself for the first time in her life.

Suddenly her tone turned defiant. "Oh, don't you entertain what you call alcoholics at your home?" The defiance, irony, and skepticism in this remark indicated that she had made a great personal sacrifice to come to my home on a weekend, to limit herself to a single drink at dinner, and to unburden herself of her personal problems.

This is not unusual to counselors who have worked with alcoholics. One must remember that alcoholism is a disease unique in that the patient at first does not want to get well. He will imply that in making the effort to comply with the necessary abstention from drinking he is doing others a favor.

Lisa talked at first abut her childhood, dwelling upon her mother's insistence that she was going to be good, beautiful, desirable, and popular.

"Think of that," Lisa said. "Me, a little pop-eyed kid, dressed up to the teeth in frills and laces and curls, trying to imagine myself to be the most popular girl in our neighborhood. You know what it leads to, don't you?"

She did not spare herself in telling about her childish attempts to be popular, and her failures. She understood why she had hit upon scholastic achievement to gain the attention she couldn't get because of her handicap.

"I guess I was poisonous, at that," she said. "I always had all the right answers in class. I won the prizes in any intellectual competition at school. But it wasn't any great satisfaction to me. I wanted to be popular. I wanted boys to be calling me for dates. And it didn't happen that way, not until I dreamed up ways to attract their attention. Inside I was so shy and conservative it was painful.

"I practiced for hours in front of the mirror to hold my head so that my weak eyes were not apparent. I wouldn't wear corrective glasses. Every move I made was calculated in advance.

"I guess I was clothes conscious before any other girl in the girls' school I attended. I studied what the popular girls wore and how they behaved, and I went them one better.

"This was the period when I was the daring and unconventional girl. It was the period when I learned that boys talk about the girls they date. They talk about how they neck and what they drink and how much.

"I let the boys know that I drank beer and cocktails by the simple expedient of getting blotto at one of the school dances. Remember, I was a scholastic standout, so that when the headmistress passed judgment on the incident she immediately assumed that it had been unintentional—that someone had spiked my punch or something like that. But word got around that little Lisa drank and necked, and you have no idea how popular I became.

"None of this, of course, proved helpful to me as a person or as a popular date. When the boys found out that I wouldn't go all the way with them, they dropped me quickly, and I was back in the same old rut.

"But at that school dance when I got drunk I had discovered something. I wasn't under that incessant pressure to act out a part, to cover up a defect which, I learned very much later, wasn't as noticeable as I thought it was."

Lisa talked and I listened, asking a question now and again to keep her in the stream of reminiscence about her girlhood.

"You are going to ask me pretty soon why I haven't married and gotten out of the rat race. Well, the truth is that I wouldn't have those who asked me, and the men I truly wanted either didn't ask me because I pushed too hard or weren't interested in marrying because they were already married or because I was too capricious and picky. Take the man I had dinner with tonight—and you can take him if you want to. He just wants a reasonably presentable woman to drink with him. I guess I have always known men like that—weekend drinkers who just want a drinking companion. It's funny how your social life changes when you have been on this kick for a while. There are the dull weekdays—then the drinking weekends. Oh boy! You must have something to drink in the house. Some of your guests drink, don't they?"

This was her first effort to persuade me to serve her a drink. Her resolution not to drink this weekend was being eroded rapidly, and was hastened by her talk about her girlhood.

"Oh yes," I said, "I have liquor for guests who want it. But that's different from guests who *need* it. You see, Lisa, you need it before you want it. And I am not really your hostess. I'm trying to be an objective friend to someone who has asked for help. I care enough about you as a friend to try to help personally. Shall we go on?"

"You know I could leave and say that I just remembered that I have an important engagement tomorrow morning first thing."

"Yes, you could leave, and I wouldn't try to stop you. But if you want my help you must contribute something— your time and your sincere effort."

"Oh, I can make it I think. But it isn't going to be easy."

Lisa began to disintegrate at that moment. "I guess all therapists are masochistic. They like to see suffering."

Lisa's life from childhood to the time of her acceptance of help toward recovery from alcoholism at the age of 34 contains all the elements of a classic and typical case of alcoholism. The capriciousness of Lisa, an alcoholic before she was 30, traces back directly to the subtle effect on her personality of the impairment of her vision.

It seems almost incredible that her impaired vision was not discovered as her chief psychological handicap by her parents or by her various teachers in school. The fact that it wasn't may be explained by the ways in which Lisa managed, even when quite young, to conceal her defective eyesight.

When Lisa was at last launched on recovery she had been through rather intensive psychotherapy bordering on psychoanalysis. After she had searched her memory for the causes of her sensitivity about her eyes, she had an explanation for much that had happened in her life.

There was a boy among her cousins who early in childhood had to be fitted with glasses, not only for nearsightedness, but also for strabismus, or crossed eyes. The cruelty of children is nowhere more manifest than in their unconscious cruel treatment of children who are handicapped in some way. The epithets they use are not meant to be cruel, but they hurt very deeply. Limpy, gimpy, cockeye, dummy, bunny (for harelipped children), squinty, Popeye, and so on.

Her cousin's playmates called him Owly, because of the heavy lenses and the magnified size of his eyes. Lisa became aware when she first faced the necessity of reading what was written on blackboards and what was printed in books that her eyes were weak and unreliable. But by that time she was determined not to become an object of fun. She learned to read by taking her book home, holding it almost at the very tip of her nose, and thus bringing the letters into focus. She developed a trick of narrowing her eyes to see more clearly so that it wasn't a squint but was an almost seductive droop of the lids.

To avoid being called upon to read from a blackboard she adopted little tricks like pretending something was in her eye, or dropping a pencil so that it would roll closer to the blackboard so that she could see. She developed behavior that practically condemned her to sit in the front of the classroom where teachers sometimes seat badly behaved children to keep them under strict surveillance. By the time Lisa was ready to graduate from grammar school she was as thorough a little phony as you could find. In addition to a difficult set of rationalizations and tricks she was also secretly contemptuous of adults she had fooled. As an only child she manipulated her parents and quite cleverly directed their attention away from her defective vision. Instead of a slight handicap, Lisa had a full-blown neurosis.

Late in her attendance at a girls' preparatory school, which she got through by the simple stratagem of borrowing her schoolmates' notes for various classes and squinting at them in secret in her own room, she was almost detected when a surprise eye examination was given to the entire student body. Somehow she managed to get out of the room and escape the scrutiny of an ophthalmologist.

By that time Lisa had convinced herself of the wisdom of Dorothy Parker's couplet that men made no passes at girls who wore glasses. She had considered getting contact lenses, but when an ophthalmologist whom she had consulted in secret told her that the contact lenses, because of the nature of her visual defect, might not be effective without long and careful treatment and experimentation, she gave up that idea.

When Lisa discovered what alcohol did for her anxieties, most of which stemmed from her foolish and frantic efforts to hide a simple eye defect, she was overjoyed. From a wary, suspicious, and introverted girl, she would blossom into a vivacious and even seductive person, eager for fun and for social contacts.

Her parents were astounded when a couple of boys brought her home from a school dance helplessly drunk. The boys were apologetic but they said, "We just couldn't stop her."

That was the pattern of Lisa's early drinking. They just couldn't stop her. The tricks and stratagems that had worked so well to cover up her visual defect, now worked even better to cover up her drinking.

She had started out to confront a drinkless weekend with brimming confidence that there was nothing beyond her powers of control. Over and over again she had assured me that when she wanted someting she had implacable determination. She talked steadily for three hours about her childhood and girlhood.

But now her determination was oozing away. The focus of her concern constantly shifted from her remembrance of the many things that had made her dependent upon alcohol to the present overriding need to anaesthetize her inner conflicts.

This need confronted her with a dilemma. She could walk out and thereby admit that she didn't have the inner fortitude of which she had boasted to see herself through one weekend without a drink. Or she could try to wheedle a drink out of me, even beg for a drink to settle her nerves.

It was important which choice she made because upon her choice would depend the alternatives that would have to be chosen to reinforce her waning determination to stop drinking.

"How would you like some coffee?" I asked her.

Lisa made a face. "I'd rather have a drink," she said. "Look, do I have to beg for a drink?"

"You will be talking to yourself if you do. I won't hear you."

"Well that's nice."

"Lisa, it may sound rude, but that's the way it has to be."

"Oh, I'll forgive you," she answered with ironic emphasis.

"I'm sure you will, but what you need to do now and for the next twenty-four hours is to go through this weekend without a drink. Why not try it until tomorrow morning, and then we can see what a new day brings?"

"Sunday," said Lisa. "Oh, I've faced that before. The bars open at one o'clock and you have to pay premium prices for bottles at drug stores. I'll try it your way."

She paced the floor, talking, pulling at her fingers so that her knuckles cracked. It wasn't coherent talk because most of what she said was clipped from the fringe of hysteria.

At one moment she would be trying to get to me with sly questions and rude criticism of my personal appearance, my manners as a hostess, the arrangement of my house, and then she would be pleading for forgiveness and imploring me to help her.

"Why do you bother with me?" she demanded. "Why? I haven't even told you the truth. How could you help me if you don't know the real facts?"

"I am not a psychiatrist, Lisa. All that I can do for you is help you to choose what is best for you, help you to make decisions that will be your own and which will be based on actuality, not on wishes and rationalizations."

"I'll tell you one thing that isn't a rationalization. I need a drink. Do you understand that? I need a drink."

"I am sure you think you do Lisa, and if you get through tonight without one you will need a drink just that much less tomorrow."

It went this way hour after hour. She refused to go to bed and she was determined that I would stay awake with her.

"You invited me here to talk," she stormed. "And by God you are going to talk with me."

About three thirty in the morning she began to weep and she stumbled with weariness as she paced the floor. Once she held her arms out to me as if imploring me to hold her like a child, but she quickly drew herself up and continued pacing from room to room.

At last she sat down on the divan and, exhausted, toppled over and lay awkwardly with one arm bent beneath her. She slept. I covered her with a steamer rug and left her there. I went to bed, worn out.

On Sunday I wakened suddenly, startled by an unfamiliar sound. Someone was humming a tune in the kitchen and hurrying back and forth in high heels.

Lisa looked up when I appeared in the kitchen door.

"Oh," she said, startled, "it's you. I was making breakfast for you."

"How do you feel?" I asked.

"Awful," she said. She saw me glance at the cabinet where the whiskey was kept. "Don't worry, I know where it is and I haven't touched it. I think maybe I'm going to make it but Lord you really shook me up last night."

As we were drinking coffee she said in a very small voice, "Do you mind if I ask you a rude question?"

"No, go ahead."

"Do you enjoy seeing people suffer?"

"No Lisa, I don't enjoy any of this. But I know that you have to go through it and it's best to have someone with you who understands."

"I'll never forget you and what you've done."

But I knew differently. She would not only forget but in the months and years ahead if she remained sober she would put out of her mind completely the long hysterical night, the things that she told me about herself, and instead would substitute a kind of hazy, half-remembered recollection of making a great decision and sticking to it. How and why she made the decision would sink into the past, and only when she was older, more secure and more mature, would the details of her decision making come back.

Meanwhile Lisa had a distance to travel before she reached security and serenity. She would be in need of more understanding and more help, but I thought she was going to make it.

There is a time in the drinking history of every alcoholic when he reaches a point of surrender, a willingness to give up his effort to manage his disordered life and to seek the help of someone he feels understands his problems. In Lisa's life one might have chosen the agonized hours when she reached for a phone in a hotel room, calling for help—this resembled a kind of surrender. But the reality can be disappointing and even frustrating to one who tries to help.

It seemed to me on my first interview with Lisa that sensibly she had decided to cooperate and make an effort to give up drinking. But she had a half pint of liquor in her handbag when she had her first interview and she had been told that her first decision in a program of recovery was what she was going to do with the liquor.

She hadn't made any dramatic gesture of giving it to me to dispose of, or of pledging not to use it. I felt fairly certain that she was going to drink it and that she wouldn't be ready to make the effort until some other crisis occurred.

When a year had passed and she finally did ask for another appointment it was important to notice the change in her manner—specifically her imperious and rude way of asking for help. The crisis had occurred. She had been arrested for driving an automobile while drunk. This interfered with her mobility, her job, her weekend drinking dates —and she faced a crisis that was meaningful to her.

On the first occasion when she asked for help she was sick and frightened. On the second occasion she saw that the phony façade of her life was falling apart and that she wasn't someone special but just a woman in her thirties who had been arrested as a drunk by policemen. In her own frame of reference this was a far more traumatic experience than waking up sick and hung over in a hotel room after a binge. She had finally been publicly exposed and humiliated.

The Lisa who woke up early that Sunday morning in my house to say that she would never forget what I had done for her was a different Lisa from the one who had paced the floor like a caged animal the night before. It had taken a year for her to reach her actual point of surrender. With honesty and humility she would make it safely to secure recovery.

Lisa's rather complicated neurotic behavior indicated complexities of alcoholism and the need for psychiatric treatment—which she responded to after several months of professional therapy. She has associated herself with an A.A. group and is doing very well with this combination of help. Indications are that there is one woman alcoholic for every five male alcoholics. The woman alcoholic presents a difficult problem to therapists because sexual behavior and emotional crackups play a greater role in the development of alcoholism in women. The women alcoholics under treatment today are not living on the fringes of society. They are mainly young and middle-aged matrons with families, hidden in unhappy homes in suburban America. The earlier they seek help, the better their chances of recovery.

CHAPTER FIVE

The Man Who Failed

Anyone who has paused for refreshment at the nineteenth hole will recognize Don or someone like him, for our golf economy with a membership of hundreds of thousands of social drinkers has those members who spend more and more time in the bar and less and less time on the course. Don was not a drinking duffer, but a master of the game—a performer whose scores were a course record in half a dozen nationally known competitive courses. The only place around a golf club where Don was the greenest kind of duffer was at the nineteenth hole.

In his mellow moods, usually that difficult time coming off a bender when he would talk almost compulsively about what he had been, Don would say ruefully, "I can handle my drinking very well. It's sobriety that throws me."

Don was more than a skilled golfer. In golf gab sessions some of his inspired moments are remembered with respect. Champions who are still active were his sympathetic confidants. They said that Don's book on golf bore the stamp of authority, particularly on the question of correcting a faulty swing.

Men who competed against him when he toured the pro circuit in competition will recall that Don wasn't a team player. He wasn't particularly good as an instructor because he seemed to be contemptuous of the learner. He was witheringly sarcastic when he was drunk. He frequently stormed into the bar at country clubs fuming, "Can't play today. The fairways are covered with sheep—only they don't know they're sheep."

Don came seeking help after he was no longer welcome

on the famous courses and the better country clubs because of his drinking.

He had a rough kind of candor when talking about himself and was excessively self-critical. "You know me all right," he said. "I'm everybody's friend and my own worst enemy, which I seem to have heard only a couple of thousand times." He waited for me to respond.

"Let's say I don't recognize you from that description," I said and smiled. "But if you have to have an enemy it might as well be you. At least you know your enemy."

"That's the trouble with those easy putts," he said. "They miss the cup. I better come right out with it."

"I think that's a good idea."

"I've got to do something about booze. Get back on my feet and make something of my life."

"Tell me something about your drinking problems," I suggested. "If we can arrange something for you it will have to be on the basis of knowing something about the problem."

"My life story—in a simple sentence. It all came too easy."

"You mean your skill as a golfer?"

"Yes. That came too easy and I didn't take care of it."

He talked softly, almost in a whisper. He asked for a glass of water, took a sip, cocked an eyebrow and said, "This stuff's no good for the kind of thirst I have. Nothing is any good for that—not whiskey, not women, not anything. Look, I know men who have given their whole lives, every waking moment to practice in order to excel at golf. I've taken money from pros who weren't half as good as I was when I was eighteen, but they practised and they learned and they grew. I didn't.

"I didn't have to work very hard. I had good coordination—good! Mine was the best. My father taught me the game from the time I was big enough to heel-in a divot, and

I played the best and trickiest courses from my teens onward. This natural swing of mine was perfect when I was
just a kid hanging around the pro shop.

"The great courses were like a lesson in geography to
me. I learned about them from my father. He knew every
lie, every possible hazard at the best of them and he taught
me. I never even considered how much effort the average
golfer puts into acquiring skill and form and a handicap.

"The adulation I got! You wouldn't believe it. Men
twice my age waiting for an opportunity just to talk to me. I
figured I was God's gift to golf."

He sat silent for a while, lost in the memory of what he
had been. His hands touched the worn spots on his gray
flannels, the bedraggled knit tie, the shabby sports coat.

"They begged me to play with them. There's a time,
you know, when adulation like that disgusts you. You see I
didn't place very much value on the coordination that I had,
and which I didn't acquire by hard work. I set out to take as
many of the suckers as I could."

Every golf pro of any stature experiences occasional
noisy approaches from golfers who want to be able to say
that they played the champ, and who secretly believe they
are good enough to take him. They will often bet substantial
sums on this delusion, and the usual outcome is that they get
what may be considered a very expensive golfing lesson.
Usually they accept the loss of their money with good grace,
knowing that they asked for the shellacking.

Don had had more than his share of such experiences.
But, from his account of it, his opponents seemed to have
believed that they had been "hustled" into the match and
taken by a slick operator. I gathered that much of this bitter-
ness was Don's fault because he admitted that when he
drank, which was almost daily, he had a caustic and biting
tongue, and frequently in the club bars he was openly
contemptuous of the men whose money he had won. In time

Don's reputation became known throughout the world of golf.

"I said I'd show them, they couldn't insult me. They bet their money and they lost it. My skill as a golfer was no secret. It was in the record books. They lost and they cried baby. I'd show them."

And show them he did—how to destroy that splendid coordination that made him a superb player; how to destroy a reputation; how to wander alone from club to club, trailed by the shadow of alcoholism and a reputation for clipping duffers. As time went on he couldn't stay very long in one place. He had to avoid people to whom he owed money.

Because he was an athlete, and because his drinking had landed him in the D.T. ward of a charity hospital only a few months before he asked for help, I arranged for a physical examination before further treatment. An internist who was also a golfer examined Don free of charge and pronounced him in excellent health, considering his age. The doctor suggested Don take Antabuse to reinforce his decision not to drink, since he had been unable to stay sober for more than a few weeks at a time.

There was one disquieting thing about Don's visit to the doctor—his contemptuous attitude. "I guess I still have some of that old magic. I paid him off with an autographed copy of my book and you'd have thought I gave him a matched set of irons. What he doesn't know is that I have a trunkful of those damned books."

The sponsor who took Don to his first A.A. meeting was an ardent golfer, happy to be of service because Don, a champion among golfers, was his "pigeon." And Don flourished as an A.A. member. I know now that it was because, despite the anonymity of the program, he found some of the adulation he had received when he was younger. During the two years that he stayed sober in A.A. he resumed living with one of his wives. (He had had three, two divorced and one who had died.) She was a bright, bustling kind of person who had travelled the golf circuit with him in the days when he was a competitor. She was able to recognize the signs and head off a drinking episode when Don became restless and irritable. He saved money from work as a golf instructor at a public course, bought an automobile, operated a small sporting goods store, and did very well. He gave up taking Antabuse because he felt secure enough to stay sober on his own. And then suddenly he sold the store and the automobile and cleared out. His A.A. sponsor heard that he was on a wild bender.

Don's wife came to me and asked for help in finding him. "I made a home for him, the first home he has had since we were divorced nine years ago, and now he does this."

Nine months later a letter stamped with the censored seal of a correctional institution revealed Don's whereabouts. He had been arrested and convicted on the charge of cashing a series of bad checks in hotels and bars. I wrote that we would be glad to see him again after his release.

When I did see him I could see how much he had deteriorated. He had lost all signs of pride. His candor had changed to cupidity.

"How did it happen, Don?" I asked. "You were getting along fine. Two years of sobriety. You must know why you did it, and I'm sure it was something more than a sudden impulse to drink."

"Sure, I know why," he said. "You talked to her and you know her kind. She smothers me. I didn't want to remarry her regardless of how much she tried to convince me I needed her. I kept thinking about all the headaches and heartaches I had with her, and all the things I did to please her, and she always demanded more. You may not agree with me, but I think some women are not people. She isn't people. She's a police dog."

"You said she wanted to help you. I'm sure she loves you, Don. If you had remarried you would have had someone close to you who really cares what happens to you."

"Yes, but people who want to help you don't watch you all the time just waiting for you to reach for a drink so that they can go into the dewy-eyed performance. She would have made a great private eye. You know how you can feel that someone is watching you. I could feel that beady eye drilling right through the back of my head even when I was asleep. The eye at the keyhole. God! She kept saying she would help me not to drink, but she made it sound like a life sentence with a warden at the door. It was too much for me so I cut out."

This was my second encounter with Don. In each of his periods of sobriety, which became shorter as time went on, there was a woman involved. He had a quixotic kind of gallantry, and his relationships with women were without sexual involvement. Here is a sample of his kind of gallantry.

He was in need of hospitalization to stop drinking and it was arranged by my office for him to go into a hospital to be treated under an Aesopian diagnosis. But he wouldn't go. He had himself admitted at the county house of correction and sweated out withdrawal in a cell. When I went to see him there I asked him why he had rejected hospitalization.

"Well," he said with a wry grin, "up in the medical ward where they send the drunks in that hospital you wanted me to go to is a tubby, good natured innocent probationer. I think she kicked off her button shoes when she came off the Nova Scotia boat on her way to nursing school. Last time I was there she got all moony over me. And I got her into trouble with the head nurse. I tricked her into leaving a jar of blue heaven [blue tinted alcohol] at my bedside table and I drank it all. They punished her for carelessness, and I just couldn't go back and face that baby-faced blue-eyed kid."

Don's gallantries were always that improbable. The only women he could tolerate were those who treated him like a loved wayward son or lover. To them he would direct all his considerable charm, all his immature appeal as a dependent male. They asked nothing of him except his mannerly flattery to brighten their lives (these were sometimes raffish lives) and he seldom had a problem obtaining shelter, at least not until he was deep into the chronic, terminal phase of the disease.

He had a succession of jobs of diminishing status and recompense and began asking for loans that he had no intention of repaying.

"Why not go back to A.A.?" I urged him some time later when he turned up to ask for a loan. "You made it once in A.A. and stayed sober for two years."

"No, I'll never go back that way again," he said. "Never play return engagements once you've been licked."

"You know that there are people who don't make it the first go around. Why not try it again? You might discover some changes—find a lost ball."

But he wouldn't go back to A.A. He had found a way of life and it became increasingly apparent that he intended to follow it. From time to time a landlady from some rooming house would turn up to explain tearfully how much she had done for Don. Inevitably there was a story of captivation by Don's eloquence and charm, of forgoing room rent because Don was such a gentleman, of feeding him when he was broke and hungry, and of buying him liquor when he had the shakes. One fading widow had pawned her rings for him.

Once, impatient with his repetitious explanations of why he drank, I said to him, "Don, you are always telling me how much you despise the drunks on Skid Row. How are you any different?"

"I am different because I was once somebody," he said. "They only pretend. They are not even has-beens."

"No," I replied, "that's not the difference. Those who were once somebody as you say, have discovered that fame is not always fortune. They may have preferred to forget it. You won't let yourself forget temporary highlights and make the effort to turn what you do know to advantage."

"I always find the easy way, don't I?" he said.

"You have found the hardest way of all."

At last Don no longer visited my office. No longer did landladies come with their news of another bender. And then there was a short paragraph in the newspaper. It did not mention that the man who died in an alley on a bitterly cold night at the age of 55 was all that was left of a once great athlete. The police had his personal possessions—a tattered copy of the book he had written about golf and four pencils lettered in gold "The Swinging Pro." Perhaps a few people remembered that he had once been instrumental in improving their swing.

What was it that made it impossible for Don to accept permanent sobriety as a means of putting his life in order? The reasons he failed and died in such sorry circumstances must be understood if the experience is not to reinforce a deep doubt that many alcoholics and nonalcoholics have about the chances of an alcoholic recovering and remaining sober.

There are many clues to why Don failed. In the first place he wasn't a great competitor, because his proficiency at golf had come to him too easily. He didn't have to strive to perfect his game. He lacked the tough realism that professional athletes must acquire to control the destructive effect of their own egos. Don believed his press clippings.

By the time he had become a compulsive drinker, only a disaster in his life—a crisis he could not handle without asking for the help and consideration of others—would have been meaningful enough to motivate him. The crises he had experienced were always eased for him by women—his wives, his girl friends, his landladies—and sometimes by golf acquaintances who would go to the rescue of the Swinging Pro. Don was never able to understand clearly that he was, in effect, a social parasite and that if he wanted to get well he would have to change his pattern of living off others. The only lesson he had learned in his life was that when he was without companionship, friends, respect, adulation, the bottle was there, waiting.

Don actively resisted learning that he needed people, that people were not patsies to be taken and exploited and discarded. He never discovered the difference between friends and admirers. Somehow, looking back across the years to his teens when he was the golden boy of golf, I know that the man who failed, failed then.

CHAPTER SIX

Route Maps to Recovery

The phrase, coming to a crisis, applied to an alcoholic may be hyperbole if one assumes prematurely that the individual alcoholic has recognized that he has a disease and is in need of treatment. One must distinguish between the true crisis in the alcoholic's life and the pseudo-crisis that has not truly shaken the foundation of the alcoholic's behavior.

Recognition and admission by an alcoholic of the true cause of acute distress and spreading disorder in life is by no means a guarantee that the alcoholic will cooperate in treatment and strive for sobriety with every fibre of being. We can only think of recognition, admission, surrender—call it what you choose—as a turning point. If the constructive steps toward recovery thereafter indicate a growing insight coupled with determination to overcome the addiction to alcohol, one can look back on the turning point and say, "Yes, the improvement began at that point and has gone on steadily since then." This is true even if the individual has relapsed once or twice while continuing to strive for enduring sobriety and release from the imprisonment of alcoholism.

From the New Orleans hotel room where Bill Barrett experienced the terror and pain of withdrawal symptoms to a low-keyed discussion of his own feelings about addiction to alcohol is a greater distance than one imagines from the telescoped account given here. The suffering and terror of withdrawal does not always provide motivation to take decisive steps to stop drinking. Some experience severe withdrawal symptoms more than once and continue to drink. Alcoholics, as examples of sick people who at the outset of treatment do not want to get well, believe that they can continue to drink by doing it carefully, skillfully, and with firm control. Sometimes this belief remains a secret obsession well into several years of sobriety.

When Bill Barrett carried out his agreement to talk about himself with a counsellor he was a likeable, humorous, outgoing man, conscious of his charm and his skill at repartee. He liked to think of himself as an extrovert. He was the stereotype of a successful salesman, even though salesmen—successful or not—cannot be stereotyped by extroversion. Some solemn and introverted salesmen have been alcoholics too. The common denominator of the high rate of alcoholism among salesmen seems to be the competitive struggle, not the individual personality.

Bill was the sort of man who knew the many ways to stand forth in a social group, to occupy the center of the social stage rather than be a quiet participant and observer. He was the kind of conversationalist who keeps his small talk abreast of all the latest quips, the most amusing badinage, and who maintains a stock of jokes and anecdotes both off-color and for use in mixed company. But he was also an alcoholic who had not been very skillful in the rationalizations he had made to protect his drinking.

He went through his routine letter perfect—like a stand-up comedian who has memorized all his material and can deliver the punch lines by rote.

"Actually I don't drink as much as my wife thinks, you know. Oh, once in a while I may go overboard, but usually it's just a cocktail or two. I gave up trying to keep the distilleries on three shifts a long time ago. The little woman gets alarmed easily. And I love her for it. But she gets alarmed and goes into a flap.

"Believe me, I couldn't rank number one on the sales force if I hit the tea as hard as she thinks I do. . . ."

His assurance began to run down, however, when his

sales pitch drew no response except a slight smile, a nod of the head, or a noncommittal, "Hm, yes, I understand what you mean."

Finally he said, "You really don't believe any of this, do you?"

"Frankly, no. I believe that this is the way that you would like it to be. But I am sure you know that isn't the way it is at all. I think that quite a while ago you began to have some doubts about the way you drink. I don't think you have said anything about it to anyone, and I don't expect that you will take me into your confidence as yet. But, there are certain things that you should know, and do, if only to safeguard your health and make yourself more secure in your job. . . ."

"Well," he said, "without making any admissions at all just suppose that I did have some trouble with drinking. I guess you'll admit that stopping is easier said than done."

"Yes, it is difficult. But it's not as difficult as life will become if something isn't done about it. And it's not nearly as difficult as you think it is at this moment. It's up to you to decide whether or not you have any trouble with drinking. For instance, a normal drinker, one who can drink or leave it alone, doesn't usually have blackouts and doesn't usually have withdrawal symptoms. A normal drinker doesn't have the shakes, and the wife of a normal social drinker doesn't get into such a flap that she rushes from Boston to New Orleans to help her sick husband who has called from a city where he wasn't supposed to be. You have experienced too many of the things that do not usually happen to the casual social drinker. Don't you think?"

"O.K. So I have trouble. What do I do?"

"Accept some treatment and learn something about alcohol and alcoholism. Does this make you angry?" He had made an impatient gesture.

"No, but you must be kidding. Learn something about

alcohol and alcoholism. Excuse me but what do you think I've been doing?"

"How much do you actually know about your body and how it utilizes alcohol? Have you ever given it any thought? How much do you know about the progressive nature of alcoholism?"

"Now that you put it that way, I'm not sure."

"Do you really want to make the effort to stop—I don't mean just until you are dried out, but stop for good?"

"At this point I don't have much to lose. So, I'll give it a try."

And so he went to a hospital to dry out, to restore his physical well-being. He decided to take Antabuse as a reinforcement to keeping his decision to give sobriety a real try. Antabuse is a Danish discovery. It is one of several kinds of chemical fences useful in motivating alcoholics to give up drinking. Taken regularly it sets up a condition in which any alcohol ingested will cause flushing, heart palpitation, extreme physical distress—a distress Bill had experienced in the hospital when he was given a test dose after he had been found physically fit to use the drug. Five days of bed care dried him out, and his first counseling session was scheduled.

But there was more than the physical effects of alcoholism to consider. This was explained to Bill at the first meeting after he left the hospital.

The reasons for his dependence upon alcohol not only had to be found, but had to be recognized and understood by him. He might know the answers and be willing to apply them, but perhaps the answers would have to be gathered slowly and carefully from those who knew him best.

"We will work on it," I said.

"We?" he asked.

"You, the doctors, your wife, your children, your relatives, me, and maybe a clergyman—perhaps you may find some help in A.A. from someone who has had similar expe-

riences. You make the decisions. We help you keep the decisions firm."

"Let's have a drink on that."

"Then it's agreed. We will have a drink on that.
Coffee?"

"I take mine black without sugar," he said with a grin.
"If it works I'll save some money. Eighty-five cents a shot.
That's a good return."

Bill didn't reveal much of his true feeling about staying
sober, but he didn't do very much cheerful grinning for a
few weeks. He was conscious that he was under surveillance. His wife hovered in the background, making
small soothing sounds, following him from room to room as
he wandered about restlessly during those periods when
some little crisis would remind him how quickly it had
yielded in the past to the effect of a drink.

"Stop playing detective," he said irritably to his wife.

She rushed to the counsellor with the tidings of Bill's
flareup. "I'm afraid he's going to drink," she said. "He told
me to stop following him around, and I just know he has a
drink hidden somewhere."

"Aren't you overprojecting?" I asked. "If he's taking Antabuse you can be sure you will know if he drinks."

"But I know the signs. He gets restless and irritable and
then he drinks."

"Following him around and snooping on him isn't going
to make him less irritable. Ask him if he'll drop in for a chat
and I'll see what I can do. But try to trust him and trust his
judgment. He is trying."

Bill expressed himself vividly and profanely when he
appeared for the "little chat." Things were going all right on
the job and he was taking his Antabuse but he was asking
questions about the medication.

"I hear there's a way to beat that Antabuse," he said.

"Where did you hear that?"

"Oh, I was talking to a fellow at an A.A. meeting."

"So you decided to try an A.A. meeting?"

"Yeh, I followed your suggestion, but I can't say I'm impressed. What do they want to tell drunk stories for? I know drunk stories that would fry their ears but I don't see the point of telling them."

"You'll understand it, I'm sure, when you find the group that suits you. You have to visit several A.A. groups before you find the right one. It probably happens that the group you visited just like to tell drunk stories to keep their common problem in front of them. I am more interested in what you said about beating Antabuse."

"Oh, I heard that there were some pills you could take to beat Antabuse—that you wouldn't have the palpitation and so on if you drank."

"Well, Antabuse is only a chemical fence to help you. You can always climb over a fence. The real test is whether you want to bring the drinking problem under control for good."

"I won't bring it under control if I'm followed around like a felon on parole. I'm sick of getting those sidelong looks. And, by the way, I've had a tough time explaining to my friends and customers why I'm not drinking. I can tell you I've made some mighty big sales over a highball in the past."

"Try telling them the truth. Just say you found it was a question of health—which it is. Have you had any big crisis at work that you couldn't handle?"

"I have never seen a big crisis yet that I couldn't handle. It's all the little problems—a hotel bill here, a dunning letter there, a funny laugh from a competitor when I refuse a drink—a lot of things like that, and they make me want to have one big smashing highball. Boom! And all my troubles will be rubbed out."

It was probable that Bill was going to relapse. Sooner or

later he would pile up enough small problems to make one big snowball the size of an avalanche and it would start a drinking episode.

When it finally happened Mrs. Barrett had been coached on what to do and how to do it.

Bill got progressively more irritable and restless. He began inventing errands to get out of the house. He was working an old trick, conditioning his wife and family to expect him to put on his hat and coat and stroll out. Each time, as he reasoned, they would expect he was going out to buy a drink, and each time he came back avoiding a strong breath in their direction he conditioned them a little more to accept his coming and going without explanations.

The day before Bill took off for a weekend with the explanation that he had to be in Syracuse to meet a couple of customers on Sunday because they were leaving for the Far West early Monday morning, his wife began packing her bag.

"What's the bag for?" Bill finally asked. "This is a business trip. I'd like to take you along, of course."

"Oh, I don't expect to go with you. The bag is packed for when you come back."

"What do you mean by that?"

"Simply this, Bill. When you come back, or when you telephone me to bring you back, I just won't be here. I won't be here ever again."

Bill departed for Syracuse on a Friday night in a black and rebellious mood. He was drunk before he took a plane at the airport. And by Saturday night the Syracuse hotel knew that they had a hospital case on their hands. He didn't telephone to his wife this time. He telephoned to his brother-in-law.

"Come and get me," he pleaded. "And don't tell Jan. I'll get straightened out and she won't have to know."

"She knows already," his brother-in-law told him. "She's

staying here with us. No, she doesn't want to talk to you. She says that she's through. And this time she means it."

The Syracuse drinking incident was a crisis and the expected turning point in Bill's sickness. The first result was that his employers became aware that he had started drinking again. His office was contacted by the Syracuse hotel where he had been staying to determine who would pay the hotel bill and whether Bill should be hospitalized or merely turned out into the street as soon as he became sober.

Bill was taken to a nursing home in Syracuse and kept there for ten days. When he returned home it was to a very painful interview at his office. The ultimatum given him left no doubt about his future.

"Either you get some treatment, Bill," said his boss, "and stay with it, or we terminate your connection with this firm. We cannot afford to have one of our employees running around the country drinking himself into insensibility."

And his situation at home was bad. The house was empty and beginning to show two weeks of dust. The newspapers had drifted into a pile of soiled newsprint on the front porch. A line of milk bottles containing sour milk was on the back porch and a note fluttered from one of the bottles saying, "I didn't get a notice you would be away. The Milkman."

Sitting before the television set in a lonely and dusty house, bottle and glass in hand, didn't inspire him with any fresh ideas on how to get his wife and children back. He finished the bottle and went to bed. His report on the bleakness of his outlook was given in person the next day when he appeared, sick and crushed, and—typical of alcoholics—unannounced.

"I'm licked," he said. "I'll really make the effort to stay sober if Jan will come back. Look, she'll listen to you."

Bill lit a cigarette. His hand trembled. He was haggard and gray. Each breath was a deep shudder.

"I guess I have been pretty much of a nogoodnick," he said at last. "I guess I can't expect Jan to take any more."

"No. You can't. And you haven't been any more of a nogoodnick than many other top salesmen who have had the same illness."

"You're kidding me. Who'd trust me now? Look, it wasn't as if I didn't know. . . ."

"I'll trust you, for one, because I think you have learned something. And there are many others who will trust you if you will show them sincerely that you are trying."

"I was trying before."

"Come on Bill, be factual. You know you weren't trying. You were pretending, marking time until you thought it would be safe to drink again. Now that should be behind you. You've learned that you can't control it."

"I'll really try to stay sober if Jan will just come back," he said. "She knows that I love her and the kids. That's the least a wife can do, to come back and help me lick this thing."

"Have you told her this?"

"Yes, I called her last night, and she wouldn't even talk to me. She just sent word by my nosey brother-in-law to see her lawyer. Is that any way to treat a man who is really trying?"

"Let's be fair. When did you decide to try? You talk as if you were trying when you tried to talk to her, but yet you say you did some drinking alone last night."

Bill hesitated and thought that over. "Well," he said after a moment, "I am ready to try."

"It takes more than just saying it. Why not make the effort for yourself. If you do it on your own she will certainly know that you are really making an effort."

"You know, there's something I don't understand. Why, all of a sudden, did she leave me? I've been in worse shape before and she didn't leave me."

"Didn't she tell you that she would leave you before you started drinking this last time?"

He then gave his version of how Jan had packed her bag as he was packing his bag to go to Syracuse, and how it had made him so angry that he took a few drinks before he got on the plane.

"But how could you take a few drinks? You were taking Antabuse. Didn't you have any reaction?"

Bill said sheepishly, "Well, I forgot to mention to you—I stopped taking the stuff a week before I left for Syracuse."

"You were planning to do some drinking then?"

"Yes, I guess I was."

"Were you really going to Syracuse on business?"

"You know I wasn't. I was going there to drink. I just had to bust out. I couldn't see that taking that medicine was doing me any good."

Plainly Bill wanted an immediate solution, a swift remedy and not a long stubborn contest with a sickness that seldom yields to sudden solutions. It was going to be difficult to persuade him that he would have to seek alleviation of his distress a step at a time—an hour, a day at a time.

First he had to be told in as gentle a way as possible that he had gone about his efforts to stay sober still wearing the alcoholic's hard indifference to the needs and thoughts of others, and that he had deluded himself with the idea that he had invincible control of himself.

"You see, the trouble is that you tried to do too much when you were not capable of such a drastic change in behavior over such a long term. The goal you set for sobriety was too distant—days, weeks, months ahead—perhaps when you thought it would be convenient. The little crises that everyone experiences in living kept chipping away at your good resolutions. You tried to keep your anxiety, tension, and vulnerability to yourself instead of talking the whole thing out with someone who could help you to understand what was going on.

"Actually we saw the possibility of a slip before you did, and we could have warned you but it wouldn't have done any good. You were cocksure that you were right and we were wrong."

"What am I going to do? No wife, no family, no job?" Bill had trouble controlling his voice.

"No one can say that you will get your wife, your children, your job back until you can demonstrate that you should have them back. When you've shown change, it would be an unreasonable person who would not recognize that you are sincerely cooperating."

"How long is it going to take? Do I have to take this all on someone's say-so? How long?"

"You'll have to find that out. I can't tell you. I don't know how much you want to change or how much effort you will put into it."

That night Bill began a long and lonely journey back to sobriety.

Jan eagerly awaited news of what Bill had said and done, and she wanted to rush back to him to help him. She had to be persuaded to let some time elapse and let him prove himself.

"There are many things you must give back to him, Jan. Things you are perhaps unaware that you took—the management of his life, his place at the head of the household, the decision to place the children in school, confidence in his own ability to stay sober. When he finally has everything under control he must have a feeling that he has done a great deal for himself, even though many people will have contributed to his understanding of his problems. Wait a while. Let him prove himself."

The solution worked out for Bill was consultation with a psychiatrist and eventual affiliation with Alcoholics Anonymous. A complete case history was given to the psychiatrist, including the tests Bill had undergone at the hospital before he was placed on Antabuse. His electrocardiogram showed no heart trouble, the doctors declared. They found his liver slightly fatty but not severely damaged. He had apparently not suffered brain damage from the attack of D.T.'s. They did find, however, that he had periods of deep-seated anxiety and depression that had to be cleared up.

After two months of regular visits to the psychiatrist—a period during which Bill had been restored to his job and had conducted a brilliant sales training program in his home office—Bill confided that he was feeling restless and edgy again. The psychiatrist explained it.

"He's lonely, and loneliness can be corrosive. He needs close companionship."

While Bill was having psychiatric treatment Jan had seen him twice, both times for dinner. They had avoided any discussion of drinking or of resuming their lives together. She was anxious to make another effort to live with Bill, but she was apprehensive that something she might do or say would trigger a slip.

Bill opened the way to a solution. "What do I have to do to prove I'm staying sober?" he asked me.

"One of the things you can do is let Jan know how you plan to insure your future sobriety. Why not attend an open meeting of A.A. together and meet some people who share some of your problems and some of your interests—both vocational and social? You'd both get something out of it."

"She wouldn't be interested," said Bill. "Besides I didn't buy any of it the last time I went."

"Suppose you are introduced to someone who will accompany you to a meeting—a couple with some of the same problems. The man I have in mind is in your line of work. Will you give it a chance?"

"What about Jan? Would she go?"

"I'll talk to her and I think she'll be delighted."

Before Jan resumed her marital relations with Bill she was asked to discuss matters with the psychiatrist. One of Bill's grievances was that she was always "serving up her successful brother" to him, no matter how Bill advanced himself in his work and in financial achievement. It had the effect of making him feel inadequate, and this inadequacy affected their most intimate relationships.

"I've been reprieved," Bill said when the psychiatrist advised him that Jan was ready to come back to him. "How long before I can say I've recovered?"

"Long enough to learn some of the things only you can teach yourself. Long enough to acknowledge that strong as you are, charming as you are, successful as you are, all this is outweighed by a single ounce of alcohol. This knowledge must become part of your whole being, your deepest consciousness. And you will know that you have hurt others as much as you have hurt yourself."

"O.K., Teach." Teach for teacher.

A note arived not long ago. "Come to dinner, Teach, if you can. We are celebrating the third anniversary of the New Orleans Mardi Gras. Jan and Bill."

Consider the problems presented by Hal, an alcoholic who voluntarily sought help. Because he seemed motivated to make an effort to recover one might oversimplify his problems and the combination of resources needed to solve them.

Therapists learn to resist any tendency to be so impressed at being chosen by the alcoholic and at achieving rapport that they discount the usefulness of any other resource except their own, and they learn not to congratulate themselves too hastily on their own discernment and skill.

Hal came to the counsellor saying that he didn't think he was an alcoholic but strange things happened to him when he drank. The immediate need was to determine whether Hal really wanted help or whether he had chosen a means of avoiding a decisive step. It is not unusual for an alcoholic to give lip service to an effort to maintain sobriety for the sole purpose of avoiding immediate unpleasantness.

People confronted with an alcoholic—and this includes members of his family—are frequently beguiled by the seeming humility and sincerity of the alcoholic's plea for help, only to discover that they have misread the true meaning of the request for assistance. For example, alcoholics may get on the phone in the middle of the night to call friends, acquaintances, family, doctors, even complete strangers, to tell how sick they are and how desirous of help. Yet it isn't the long term help such as one must have to recover from alcoholism that they seek. They want short term help to get sober. Some deeper significance can be found in the loneliness and isolation that drives an alcoholic to reveal his condition to others. Such calls for help are often for the sole purpose of hearing a human voice, or striving to maintain some sort of contact with a normal world. There was a time, before automatic exchanges, when telephone operators who responded to every call on their boards were acceptable and often badgered contacts with alcoholics—the voice at the end of the wire that gave them reassurance that someone was there. Today the dial tone lacks such comfort. The alcoholic wants a voice—a human voice.

So it is with the resources to which an alcoholic applies for help. It may only be a way station on the road to recovery. He may be motivated by a desire to shop around and see what is available. It may be a call made at the insistence of wife or relative or employer at a time when the patient needs help and is willing to take desperate measures in a desperate situation.

To accept the fact that the alcoholic has sought help as being sincere and dependable motivation to cooperate in treatment is unrealistic. One can be certain only that at the moment the alcoholic asks for help he needs help and is willing to discuss his problem with someone.

This is no guarantee that what the alcoholic discloses is the truth, or that it is sincere. Some alcoholics feel better immediately after they have confided in someone who offers a reasonable and friendly repository for the confidential information. They will have taken the first hurdle and may often begin at that moment to congratulate themselves that now that they can talk to someone about their problem they have it licked.

Hal wasn't telling the whole truth, and he put the best interpretation he could upon the facts to still remain on the borders of reality. His drinking history was not what he said it was. He was more deeply involved in compulsive drinking than he admitted. He did not want to acknowledge that he was in dire trouble.

As autobiographers, alcoholics are generally prone to literary license, particularly those who are articulate and outgoing people. An alcoholic with a sense of humor may be more difficult to counsel because he will tend to use wit as an emollient to soothe the raw hurt of rejection. If he can get you to laugh *with* him there is less danger that you will laugh *at* him. It frequently happens that personal crises are treated with irony and humor rather than as human tragedy in the making. This often presents the necessity of making a quick choice of when to laugh and when not to.

Hal employed wit very adroitly to conceal his deep anxiety and his outrage at his failure to maintain a secure place in the social structure of his group. His tone was light and self-disparaging. When he couldn't find a satisfactory explanation for some peculiarity in his personal behavior he invented a light and humorous tale to account for the abnormality. He was at the outset unable to say openly, "I was deeply hurt and determined not to let anyone pity or patronize me and so I passed it off as a joke. But it wasn't a joke. It was frightening. I needed to have someone laugh with me about it because it exposed me as an irresponsible drunk."

Many alcoholics contrive a world of fantasy in which they are reasonably comfortable and at ease. Using rationalizations as building material they contrive a kind of theatrical stage setting in which they move around in a stylized way as the principal actors in a tragi-comic play. For long intervals of time they succeed in amusing all beholders and deflecting criticism of their performances. They often prefer the characters they play to their real selves. But the time comes when there is no stage on which they can perform, when their disgust with themselves is too distressing to permit saying their comic lines. Then the fantasy falls apart leaving them lonely and confused in a great gray world and the only place to hide is in a bottle.

The first task with Hal was to give him confidence that his action in seeking help, whether its motives were self-serving or merely momentary attempts to please another's insistence on getting help, could be expanded by his own efforts into a program of treatment and recovery for which he, and he alone, could be responsible, and for which he, and he alone, could take credit.

He had given an explanation of why he sought my help. Yet without revealing to him that he needed during the next few weeks to be under observation by those who loved him most and wanted to help him, it was important to find out what his true situation was at home. Did those who were dependent upon him know the nature of the sickness that handicapped him? Would they cooperate in the treatment by leaving the therapy to the therapists? How much of his role as a producer of family income and a family decision maker remained? How much would be restored to him when and if he became capable of carrying the responsibility?

It was also important to learn what could be substituted for the social activity and release that drinking had provided

him. One of the chief stumbling blocks in therapy for alcoholic patients is that one frequently finds that they are willing and eager, at least for a reasonable length of time, to
forgo drinking. They may even have tried several times and
may have been partially successful in maintaining sobriety.
But what could they substitute for their world of fantasy,
the beguiling feeling that they were of a race of giants or
geniuses? When they were sober and matter of fact they
found life tasteless and dull. The social drinking group, itself
a snarl of prejudices and myths, would have none of them
because they had given up drinking. Those who had observed previous efforts to remain sober waited with bated
breath for them to slip. And because all the values of their
drinking behavior, all their drinking history, were oriented
to adjusting in a world that inflicted hurt, it was difficult for
them to find or accept a way of life that had interest and
flavor. Sobriety is a tasteless bread for mere existence, for it
requires complete reorientation to make a new person who
can perceive the gradual growth of a new life.

Sometimes this objective can be reached with a minimum of soul searching by those who will accept and participate in the fellowship represented by Alcoholics Anonymous. The reasons why alcoholics accept A.A. are as varied
and capricious as human behavior. The reasons why some
alcoholics reject A.A. are better known. Alcoholics can
readily go along with the disease concept of alcoholism because they learn with relief that they are sick people. It ex-
plains for them much of what they have been told is moral
weakness. It is when they are faced with the need for "surrender to a Higher Power" that they begin to shy away from
A.A. To benefit from A.A. association one needs basic intelligence, and this doesn't mean education. One also needs to
learn as a child learns—from example. But most necessary is
the acceptance of a need to draw upon a spiritual deposit
made to one's account at birth for the means to invest in a

sober, healthy life—to eke out the expenditure of this with-drawal from the spiritual bank account a day at a time until the whole interrelationship of the A.A. program has pro-vided its healing.

In a materialistic world where people are often spirit-ually bankrupted at a very early age, it is difficult for many men and women to place their faith in a "Higher Power" or in a "Power greater than themselves." This is not to say that with proper treatment and personal development they can-not come at last to the priceless supportive association for alcoholics in A.A. But, I do say that if the patient is skeptical of spirituality and hostile for many reasons to reli-gious feelings, A.A. affiliation is not always possible. It is unwise to refer to A.A. without knowing whether A.A. has been accepted or is acceptable to the individual. Some mem-bers of Alcoholics Anonymous will say that such individuals have not hit bottom, or that they have not suffered enough. But this is being disproved by a large number of compara-tively young people whose sickness has not advanced to any-thing like the "hitting bottom" stage who benefit from and recover in Alcoholics Anonymous. Today the phrase "hitting bottom" is coming to mean hitting a spiritual bottom.

In counselling alcoholics one proceeds until confronted by a kind of mental roadblock set up by the patient. If the roadblock can be talked out of the way with simple under-standing of the problems, well and good. But often the roadblocks have firm foundations in the individual's con-sciousness and cannot be battered down, pushed aside, or otherwise removed except by a very delicate psychological engineering technique. Such problems belong in the hands of psychologists or psychiatrists, remembering all the while that no one discipline has all the answers.

Throughout contact with Hal there was a persistent and definite impression that neither Hal nor Elsa had told all the essential facts. There was Elsa's expression of distaste when

she had told how Hal drank until he fell down on the floor
and her statement in the same breath that she had a baby
and was frightened. There were Hal's sudden silences when
the conversation got around to Elsa. "She will tell you a lot
of things about me that aren't pretty," Hal had said.

None of Elsa's discussion of her husband had been what
anyone who has counselled alcoholics would call "not
pretty." It was plain that Hal's mother-in-law had interfered
in their marriage, but even this gave no clue to what was
wrong with the couple's marriage.

In several talks with Hal concerning the possibilities of
a re-examination of his marital relationship, either in pastoral counseling or by use of the services of a psychologist or a
marriage counselor, Hal's reaction was one of alarm.

"Would you consider talking frankly with someone with
professional training about your marital affairs?" I asked
Hal.

"No, I don't want to talk with anyone like that. I
haven't been to church since I was married and I don't want
to talk with any minister. And my marital relations are my
own affair. I don't think it has anything to do with this
thing."

"Do you mind if I have a talk with Elsa about this?"

"I don't know what you are talking about. Elsa's
satisfied with the two children. She doesn't care one way or
the other."

And that was all Hal would say.

Elsa, in the meantime, was reading some selected material about alcoholism which she had been given in the
hope that she could talk things over and be of some assistance in solving Hal's drinking problems.

She telephoned to inquire whether or not she could
have a conference because she felt that Hal wasn't improving as rapidly as she thought he should.

"By all means," I said. "I wondered whether you might

also want to talk the subject over with other women whose husbands have the same problem."

"I don't know about that," Elsa said. "I'll ask my mother."

"No, what I had in mind was for you, not for your mother," I said. "This group of people are not alcoholics, but they have husbands or wives who have the problem, and they are helping one another understand the problem."

"I'd rather talk to you," Elsa said.

Elsa came alone to have a talk. And I was as matter of fact as possible. First, we talked about their bills and the lack of money.

"I understand from Hal that you own your own home but that there's a big mortgage on it and you owe for appliances and things like that."

"We owe everybody. I suppose we do own the house, but the bank's going to take it."

"Well, if it were possible to increase the mortgage and get some cash, would you be able to pay the bills?"

"We need three thousand dollars at least, and who's going to lend us that?"

"Well I don't know Elsa, but I think that you should go to Family Service and take your bills along and the papers on your mortgage and see what they advise. I am sure that something can be done."

"Who do I see about it?"

"Well, I'll make a few telephone calls and I can tell you that. But, before we go into that there are one or two other things perhaps you should discuss. I am going to have to ask you personal questions. Hal didn't want to discuss marital relations. Would you talk about that to a marriage counsellor?"

"I guess I can take it. I've been embarrassed to death as it is."

"We do not want to embarrass you. But perhaps we can find something that both you and Hal have overlooked."

"All right," she said. Elsa sat silently looking down at her hands folded in her lap. She gnawed her lips and clenched her fists suddenly.

"It's simply too disgusting," she said explosively. "Disgusting. I can't stand it. It's always when he's drunk. That's the only time. Two children and both from a drunken man."

"Have you ever discussed this with any professional person?"

"No, never, and I'm too ashamed to talk about it. I talked to my mother about it as much as I could, and she said . . . Oh, it doesn't matter!"

"What did she say Elsa?"

"She said I had to expect that. All men are pigs."

"Do you think that about Hal?"

"No, but what can I think? Only when he is drunk . . ."

We sat together silent. And then Elsa covered her face with her hands and wept.

At last when she stopped sobbing I asked her, "Elsa would you like to get some very good professional advice about this? It doesn't have to be this way you know. Perhaps this is one of the reasons why Hal is in trouble with liquor. Anyway, we should find out."

"How can I do anything about it now . . . after all this time?"

"What I have in mind Elsa is to have you talk with a woman who can help you. She's a qualified clinical psychologist and she specializes in marriage counselling. A little later as Hal continues with his treatment there will be some attention given to this part of your lives together. But you will not have to discuss this with Hal. Let me make an appointment for you to see the psychologist. . . ."

"I think I should talk it over with my mother."

"Later on perhaps. But right now I think it would be best if you simply talked with the psychologist."

"I haven't any money to pay doctors' bills."

"Don't worry about that immediately. I think that after some help from Family Service and disposal of the pending debts you will be able to pay her."

Slowly the jumbled puzzle of their lives was forming a definite picture. I remembered Hal's mother, and her candor about how she had demanded so much of her own husband. Somewhere in Hal's boyhood was the reason for his feeling of sexual inadequacy, which required skills other than mine for a solution. But the solution would be final and would be achieved in the use of existing community resources.

Hal's treatment was by no means so simple as making a choice of existing community resources, and referring Hal and his wife to them. As is often the case with marriages in which alcoholism has caused derangement, Hal and his wife were not and could not be completely objective in eliminating the factors in their lack of marital adjustment that contributed to Hal's frustrations. Time was needed to keep them together, to work out a step-by-step approach to Hal's sobriety and to make them truly partners in marriage.

Elsa's revulsion with cohabitation with Hal wasn't swept away by simple recognition of what the deeper problems were. It required the skills of a professionally trained marriage counsellor whose knowledge of alcoholism and its effects on marriage included a recognition that the couple had much that could be salvaged. Hal's problems were solved at length, but he had help from a mental-health clinic, group therapy with other alcoholics, and a firm supportive association with Alcoholics Anonymous, which was of benefit to both Elsa and Hal.

Most important was the ending of interference from the two mothers who, although they only partially acknowledged their responsibility for the disruption of their children's lives, were nevertheless accountable. Hal's mother had taken his father away from him when he needed a father and had demanded too much achievement from Hal. Elsa's mother, by her failure to treat and talk to her daughter as a grownup, had contributed to her misunderstanding of sexual relations in marriage. Her comment on the porcine nature of man was an example.

The last communication from Hal and Elsa seems to sum up how well they adjusted to each other and shared the basic problems. It was an invitation to a party on their tenth wedding anniversary with a note from Elsa saying, "It should be our fifth. We really began our marriage after having two children and that trouble which we do not mention any more."

The process of recovery is for most alcoholics one of maturing and assuming a broader scope of attributable responsibilities. It sometimes seems that alcoholics are people who have aged and matured successfully in one or more of the fundamental ingredients of full maturity, and until it can be determined which ingredients are missing, alcohol serves as a substitute.

The change in them is profound when the substitution is recognized and accepted. Lisa, the young woman who spent her crucial weekend at my home, showed the kind of immaturity often found in the least complicated alcoholics— if one can assign to an alcoholic a degree of complication. Her behavior was a trial to those who knew and loved her, but she was able to maintain outside relationships almost normally. Of Lisa and her kind it is often said that they are fine persons when sober but entirely different individuals when drinking.

From this generalization it is a short and simple step to accept an erroneous belief that Lisa and those like her are psychotic to some degree when they are drinking because their immature and abnormal behavior while drinking is so markedly different from their winsomeness and charm when sober. The behavioral changes in alcoholics while drinking are certainly not to be evaluated by laymen. This is best left to the experts in psychopathology. It is helpful to observe and take note of behavioral changes, but snap judgments about what they mean must be eliminated if alcoholism is ever to be understood and effectively treated.

Yet, if Lisa's behavior is examined from her viewpoint, taking into consideration the emotional and social distress which made her vulnerable, it will be seen that Lisa's life as a compulsive drinker was a simple projection of her striving from childhood for what she conceived to be reality. There is extreme pathos in her frantic attempts to conceal a handicap, to be popular and desirable, to find a niche in society in which she could command the attention and approbation of her fellow humans. There was a point in her life—probably when she was fitted with corrective glasses—when she could have been persuaded with very little effort that girls who wear glasses are still attractive and still marry for love and live normal lives. But Lisa was further handicapped by a mother ambitious for her daughter, who lived by trivial and superficial standards, who found a daughter with weak eyesight a reflection upon her excellence, her social status, and her motherhood.

And so Lisa might never adjust to the fact that without corrective glasses her eyes would be unreliable but she would be able to live with it, accepting the unreality of her constant effort to conceal a minor handicap as reality. So it is with the majority of alcoholics who recover. Their recovery may be based upon rationalizations that will not stand up to the test of reality, but it is reality to them and they are able to handle life without recourse to the substance that beguiled and betrayed them.

It was several weeks before Lisa would look at me directly and reveal those weak squinting eyes or wear the corrective glasses except when she was secure from public exposure.

She brought herself to call attention to it. One day on the telephone she said brightly, "This is your four-eyed friend."

I thought quickly. "Which one?" I asked.

"Have you got more than one?"

"Oh, yes, many more, but only one who might think it remarkable."

There was a moment of silence. "O.K." Lisa said, "I get it."

She never mentioned it again, and from that point onward she always wore her glasses. Her ophthalmologist, unable to fit her to contact lenses, persuaded her to try decorative frames that emphasized the graceful sweep of her eyebrows.

When Lisa went to court on the driving while drunk charge and was convicted, fined, and her her license taken away, she faced the crisis with commendable calm and a week after that she was summoned to take a job as a speech therapist, for which she had qualified before taking up interior decorating.

She was working with blind and deaf children which, because of the demanding nature of the work, could create serious tension and anxiety. She wrote regularly to fill in the gaps when she was unable to talk in person.

"Think of it," she wrote. "I am in my fourth month at school. I have to get up at six in the morning because I am in a car pool. I just couldn't live at the school.

"My angels are quite pathetic because everyone seems to give up on breaking through to them. I don't get the support I feel that I need but I am philosophical about it. I think no one is hopeless—not me, not them.

"I go to A.A. meetings regularly and I can even participate, not just sit there like an image. My other friends—I call them civies—still include me in parties and dates. And it's difficult, because I don't drink.

"It helps a great deal to talk to you and write to you. I think we have a certain amount of communication because we both deal with problems. Bear with me. If I can get through this year and the next I will have won—and this is important to me. Sorry as I am for giving you such a hard time I understand a little bit that it was necessary for me to show myself to you as I was so that I could become the me that I am."

Lisa has now been sober for two years. She met the problems that sobriety brought to her life one by one. In her two years of sobriety only one serious problem has troubled her.

"I am having difficulty meeting eligible men but I am working on it," she told me. "I just can't stand those people I used to call civies. I find the fellows I used to drink with are pretty dull. Pretty dull? I mean just plain dull . . . but there's a doctor I met——um . . . well, we'll see."

One has to examine all of Lisa's rationalizations and resentments to give adequate attention to her many needs. Some references have been made to her mother's social ambitions for her daughter, her dismay over the visual handicap which she perceived as a social handicap, and the subtle but constant efforts to manage or intrude in her daughter's life.

Yet this clucking of a mother hen is not to be wondered at. And in the context of the whole picture of Lisa and her family it is understandable. In addition to psychiatry Lisa had a need to come closer to the identification of herself as an alcoholic, and not an uncommon alcoholic into the bargain. She had set herself apart from other young women, consoling herself with being brighter and more intelligent than average, and thinking that what worked for them in meeting the strains and stresses of alcoholism was too commonplace and too boring to meet her special needs.

I persuaded her to attend a closed meeting of an A.A. group in a suburban community where all of the members were not only at her own social level but many were business and professional people of even higher status than her father.

This element of snobbery in acceptance of A.A. is not unusual. In most instances it is a phase through which many recovering alcoholics pass in their development in A.A. It seemed to me, when Lisa made a few tentative efforts to take part in the discussion at the closed meeting of A.A., that she was in desperate need of understanding herself, of learning why she had turned out to be the kind of person she was. In short, she had to learn to become her own severest critic without damaging the ego which was so essential to her.

At one of the closed meetings a woman talked with stark candor about the dissolution of her marriage, her affairs with one man after another, her reasons for eventual recognition of her essential problem. Lisa, white and visibly disturbed, blurted out, "Well, I never sank that low."

The woman looked across a broad table at Lisa, smiling but with a sad quirk at the corners of her lips. "No," she said. "Perhaps no one ever sank in quite the way I did, but what is important is that it's all up here (tapping the center of her forehead). It's up here right in the middle of our judgment center, and when our inhibitions are loosed we learn that we, too, are primates, a little higher perhaps than the other tailless apes. Our trouble is that we have fewer choices of behavior when we drink, and progressively fewer as we continue to drink. What may start out as noble romance ends in self-disgust."

"Please forgive me," Lisa said.

"There's nothing to forgive," the woman responded. "It takes a little while to accept ourselves as we have been and, in knowing, become what we can be."

Several days later in the midst of a conversation not relevant to her own drinking problem Lisa said in a tone of desperation, "I will never be able to talk about the thing that I have done, oh, much worse than she mentioned, because I wanted to hurt someone or because I needed an excuse for what I was doing."

The abrupt change in Lisa's attitudes was too marked not to have been noticed by her family. Her mother, trying to understand, striving not to be excluded, decided that if Alcoholics Anonymous had wrought this change then she too would attend meetings and find out for herself why it worked and where she had failed.

Lisa came raging to me when she found her mother at an A.A. meeting. "Is there no way to get out of her clutches?" she wept. "There she sat, nodding her head in agreement with every speaker, and when she got home she began to tell me all about alcoholism, all about what was good for me. Damn her. Isn't there anything, any place to get away from her?"

At this point it became necessary not only to have a talk with Lisa's mother, but also to release Lisa to a more self-reliant relationship with Alcoholics Anonymous and her psychiatrist.

Lisa's mother was a name dropper and a tiresome person to engage in conversation. She sounded at times like a compendium of the trivialities of the social chatter columns in newspapers. But after she exhausted her current list of friends, acquaintances, social contacts, and social engagements one understood Lisa and her mother very much better.

Here was a woman whose insecurity had been handed along to her daughter. Her dreams for Lisa had been of a brilliant social figure, advantageously married, reflecting credit upon her upbringing and her family. When the child failed to conform to the dream, she had persisted in her efforts to shape her daughter's life, making of it a nightmare of petty failures to conform. As Lisa grew up and resisted the tireless efforts her mother put forth to create a social butterfly, her mother became aware that somehow she had failed as a parent. Lisa's father, who throughout her childhood had regarded his only child more or less as a part of his family's table of organization, became the preferred parent and her mother, who had put forth such extraordinary efforts to create a life and a personality for her daughter, was avoided.

"I do not understand it," she said. "It is as if she isn't my child at all. I want to help her get over this awful thing but she won't even discuss it with me. I'm her mother, after all."

"Have you thought about the fact that *you are* her mother as a reason why she cannot risk talking to you about a personal problem for which she feels responsible. Most of the people who recover from alcoholism do so because they believe that they have recovered by their own efforts, regardless of how much help others have been. It has to be this way in order for them to feel secure and confident. She may fear that you will tell her what she knows she should do. You tell me that you have been going to meetings of A.A., slipping in so that Lisa won't see you. Isn't this a kind of surveillance? Lisa might feel that you do not have any faith in what she is trying to do—that you are watching her and interfering."

"I only want to know what it is that helps her, what it is that I couldn't do for her."

"After Lisa has fully accepted a program of recovery she will be able to explain it to you. You could ask her then —she will tell you—let her take the initiative now. This will require patience on your part and a change of attitude toward Lisa. She is a grown woman, capable of supporting herself and amply equipped to make a life for herself. Let her do it."

"But all the running around she has done—all those men. And she wasn't serious with any of them."

"That's the concern of the psychiatrist who is seeing her. Let's not meddle in something which is better left in the hands of a professional."

Lisa had felt enormous guilt about an affair she had subjected herself to earlier. Such guilt, in fact, that each time she dwelt on the affair it precipitated another drinking episode.

"Were you in love with the man you have mentioned so often?" I asked her.

"Not really," she said. "I wanted to think I was, but I don't think he was in love with me, either, and I was never sure about him. I think perhaps he wanted a mother."

"Lisa," I said finally, "don't you understand that you have got to talk about this aspect of your life with the doctor? He can help you get to the heart of the problem. Right now you are staying sober in A.A., and perhaps you can continue. But if you want to be successful in this you must face all your problems, not just the drinking problem. What you tell your psychiatrist is in strict confidence. Even though I know him very well he will not disclose anything of your confidences to me or to anyone. But he has to have your confidence and your complete cooperation."

"I'll try," said Lisa. "You've been right so far."

The psychiatrist brought about a great change in Lisa's outlook. He was especially interested in the problems of exceptional children, and because Lisa had been trained as a speech therapist and had worked with children, he was able to interest her in applying her knowledge to work with exceptional children.

As she worked in this specialized field, at first as a volunteer and later as a staff member of a clinic for exceptional children, she began to talk about one child in particular, a little motherless boy whose mental disturbance dated from his mother's death by suicide when he was five years old. He hadn't uttered a word for almost three years. Lisa reported on the child's condition with more than clinical interest and then she began making passing references to the child's father. Gradually the child's father emerged from these passing references as a whole person—an ambitious, hard working electronics technician who, in addition to making a fight for his son's normalcy, was trying to improve himself with night courses at a university.

"It's amazing what he learns from just hearing me talk to little David," Lisa confided. "Some words that he mispronounced he now pronounces correctly. And he's so concerned about David. I wonder what my life would have been like if I had had a father like David's."

I laughed. Lisa looked up at me, caught my expression, and laughed herself.

"Maybe I will get a husband instead of a father, is that what you are thinking?"

"That's what I was thinking, but I wondered about your mother."

"Oh, mother! I have found out how to handle her," Lisa said. "If you just let her think that everything you do is her idea, she's happy. And this may amuse you—she told me the other day that she felt kind of left out at A.A. meetings because she can't get up and talk about her drinking problem."

When the life story of Don, the golf pro, comes under consideration one has to search for the reasons why he, an athlete who should have been supremely aware of the effect of drinking on his coordination and judgment, failed to get well. One must conclude that he accepted the help of Alcoholics Anonymous for the wrong reasons.

That he gained sobriety in A.A. was to Don's way of thinking an extra dividend. What he valued most in A.A. was really that he was accorded recognition and admiration of his skill as a golfer and a champion. It was something he had lost and missed while he was drinking. He stayed sober so that he could continue to bask in the limelight, not because he had lost control of his ability to handle alcohol. Like most people A.A. members tend to hero-worship, and to flatter those who have some special eminence in one field or another, despite the hard fact that they are all equals sharing the same personal problem. Many A.A. members who knew Don while he was in A.A. were not greatly surprised when he failed.

They did not say that his trouble was a swollen ego. They put it in A.A. lingo. He didn't have humility. He hadn't hit bottom. He would never hit bottom. In his own view he was Don the great golf champion and never Don the drunk.

One used to talking to alcoholics would have perceived in Don a mocking and ungrateful attitude toward others, an overweening pride and a peculiar blindness to the realities of his situation. Even when he had slipped to the point of living off landladies of rooming houses on Skid Row, he did not recognize that the great golfer had become a Skid Row alcoholic, even though he didn't fraternize with Skid Row drinkers.

The values he had acquired and by which he regulated his life when he was a child hanging around the pro shops and travelling the golf circuit with his father were a poor base for building personal integrity. The rehabilitation of personal integrity is a great part of recovery from alcoholism.

Don truly had never regretted any of his shortcomings,

nor did he recognize with anything more than lip service that he had harmed many people. What he *did* admit was that for him everything had come too easily. But he had a feeling that he was destined for and entitled to special favor. He expected sobriety to come to him that way too, and it eluded him.

CHAPTER SEVEN

Sips, Slips, and Relapses

An ever-present threat to health and stability of an alcoholic is a "slip." A slip in alcoholism is what would be called relapse in any other disease. Those who think in terms of moral lapses in connection with the recurrence of drinking in an alcoholic are quite likely to remark in tones ranging from compassionate to sanctimonious, "Once a drunk, always a drunk."

Relapse in alcoholism has definite physiological and psychological causes which, like symptoms of relapse in other diseases, can be detected in advance of acute symptoms and headed off by prompt and appropriate treatment.

Alcoholics and those who have the closest relationship with them are better able to deal with slips if they have deeper understanding of the causes of relapse. The more alcoholics learn of the why and how of alcoholism the less likelihood there is of a relapse.

Development of alcoholism in the individual is always accompanied by a significant and subtle difference in the rewards of alcohol to the alcoholic as compared with what the average social drinker gets from drinking. Alcoholics have secretly rejoiced that they have found a medicine which, for them, works faster and more effectively than any other in altering their feelings of depression, anxiety, tension, inferiority, timidity, fear, or whatever deficiency of body or mind may have permitted alcoholism to establish a beachhead in their personalities.

True, they chose the wrong medicine to chase away their bugaboos. While they become more and more dependent upon this medication they are less and less able to recognize that in dosing themselves with this substance they had (to quote an old phrase) engaged a fool for a physician.

For an alcoholic to achieve sobriety requires a heroic struggle—pigmy man against a titan. Every fibre of one's being seems allied against the desire to quit, and treacherously plotting against every positive decision. In the very attempt to stop drinking alcoholics build up expectation of rewards for victory other than improvement of health and brighter prospects as a person with improved judgment and a more mature outlook.

Alcoholics who find the rewards for their herculean struggle for sobriety to be less than their expectations will sometimes return to drinking declaring that their efforts deserve something more than mere sobriety. In such cases the miscalculation was expectation of some sort of magical pot of gold for making the positive decision rather than the acquisition of the solid and much to be desired tranquillity of a sober life.

Often the failure is not alone that of great expectations, but also an oversight of the counsellor who should have spelled out the true and valuable rewards of sobriety in terms which the individual could comprehend. Help is needed by the recovering alcoholic to discover the hidden potentials that will make life more meaningful. One must, however, make allowances for the variations in intellectual maturity and differences in the physical and psychological dependency of alcoholics.

Most often the relapse is rooted in the pressing demands of family, friends, or colleagues for a flashing, brilliant performance from the recovering alcoholic immediately upon the conclusion of a measurable period of sobriety. Rapid recoveries do happen, but the rapidity is only on the surface of things. The change deep down requires the healing of time.

Alcoholism takes a long time to develop in an individual. It is going to take a long time to recover and become secure enough to face up to rebuffs, disappointments, and nagging fears.

Recovering alcoholics cannot and should not be pressured to plan too far ahead. The environment of alcoholics in the process of recovery is under constant threat. The first two or three months of sobriety may bring a glow of self-satisfaction at having been able to control the drinking problem. Yet this may be like the lull in a struggle to save a sinking ship when it seems the fight is won and the ship saved. This is the time when relapses may threaten because vigilance and exertion are relaxed. Sudden illness, death of loved ones, unexpected economic pressure, and job changes present such threats to sobriety.

Alcoholics have to have reasons for continuing the fight for sobriety, for maintaining constant vigilance, for striving to accept the scuffle of life as it is rather than as one dreams it should be—if . . . That lean, attenuated "if" stands waiting inside a bottle.

People closest to a recovering alcoholic can develop an intuitive sense of change in the barometric pressure of calm sobriety. But they must be aware of situations fraught with dangers of a relapse and, without undue discussion, quietly take appropriate steps to bypass the peril.

Some of these situations may develop from what others believe are kindness and consideration for an alcoholic, which in fact only contributes to a pervading feeling of inadequacy.

The Changed Role in the Family. During development of acute alcoholism the alcoholic's role in the family undergoes gradual and sometimes destructive modification. From head and mainstay of the family a husband becomes a subordinate or dependent family member. Functions which once were his as husband and father are taken over by others. Decision making is either surrendered or pre-empted by a wife or some other adult in the family. Wives with alcohol problems are placed in a sort of purdah, their movements circumscribed, their functions as homemaker limited or shirked. They are hidden from the world's scrutiny as much as possible. Recasting the alcoholic in a family role becomes not so much a question of when he will be able to resume his former position, but whether he will be permitted to do so. Family members will often deny the husband or father the right to pick up threads of former family leadership, and will also demote the former homemaker to housekeeper. In short—he is made to feel untrustworthy or on permanent probation.

Job Frustration. Alcoholics face the realization that while they have been drinking their effectiveness on the job has deteriorated to some extent and they will have to readjust to a post with less prestige and satisfaction while they go through the long pull of rehabilitation. Discouragement and frustration are inherent in the struggle to regain respect, authority, and larger financial rewards. Two destructive labels are often unfairly attached to alcoholics who are striving to come back—the cruel "has been" and "never was."

Social Life. The recovering alcoholic whose social life has centered upon drinking occasions faces awkward situations when he begins his baffling search for satisfying and acceptable social relationships compatible with sobriety. He has terminated his associations with drinking situations and sometimes the drinking companions of his days of compulsive drinking. His old social drinking friends give only conditional acceptance because they are either ill at ease with one who does not drink with them any more, or hostile to one who poses a threat to their social drinking because he has not been able to stand the pace, hold his liquor, or play the social drinking game according to their rules. The loneliness of alcoholism can easily become the isolation of sobriety—at least temporarily—for the recovering alcoholic.

Rebuffs. Accumulations of rebuffs, slights—either real, or imagined—tactless remarks about abstinence or drunkenness, aggressive demands for the alcoholic to try "just one," having one's abstinence explained to others, and deliberate rejection all contribute to making the sober alcoholic miserable. He may tell himself, "I might as well be drunk as the way I am."

Limited Capabilities. The majority of nonalcoholics believe that all an alcoholic must do to be completely rehabilitated is to stop drinking and that immediate rejuvenation is achieved. Such views result in demands upon alcoholics far in excess of their capabilities during the early stages of recovery. Immediate miracles are beyond the power of mortals, and sometimes God is a trifle hard-pressed to bring one off.

Overconfidence. After extended periods of sobriety some sober alcoholics relax their vigilance against threats to their sobriety, and incident by incident small tensions build up into mammoth and unmanageable proportions.

Dismissing the Past. Inability to let the past go with all its unhappiness and distress provides a breeding ground for slips. It is easy to say, "Forget the past." But it is difficult to do. Alcoholics have a hard time accepting that they can do nothing to change the past and can do very little planning for the future, but they can be ever watchful in the present. Inability to forget the past results in a total lack of compassion for oneself after one has done all that is possible to make amends for past wrongs.

Dry Drunks. So-called dry drunks are experienced by many sober alcoholics. They go through complete but usually temporary recurrence of active symptoms of drinking without having taken any alcohol. This carries with it a keen arousal of feelings that a drink would immediately get rid of the suddenly unbearable fogginess and jitters. During such episodes sober alcoholics usually draw closer to their A.A. affiliation, their therapist, their physician, their clergyman, or their counsellor for support.

The Big Bang. Self pity.

Seduction. Mates of recovered alcoholics have been known to try to make their sober spouses drink again. Their prime reason for seducing the sober alcoholic to abandon sobriety is that they preferred them when they were immature and dependent. They resent the sober mate's growing self-sufficiency and stability. Both wives and husbands of alcoholic mates often enjoy wearing the crown of martyrdom. They feel that their mate's sobriety robs them of their hard-earned reputations for saintly suffering and forbearance. Some even miss the fuzzy amiability of drinking spouse, or find the change in sexual dynamics a source of discontent.

The foregoing are only a few of the areas in the anatomy of alcoholic relapse rarely discussed or understood by those close to alcoholics whose actions and attitudes will have an important bearing upon the duration of sobriety. Even alcoholics, whose experience should make them ultrasensitive to the nuances of recovery processes, sometimes overlook the menace of post-recovery situations like these. As sober alcoholics strive to find a secure place in their social group and to adapt to the environment and culture of their time, they may miss the implication of the accumulations of petty annoyances. One of the most important functions of Alcoholics Anonymous is to fill the need alcoholics have to talk out threats to their sobriety with those who share their concern.

When an alcoholic has been able to maintain sobriety

for as long as two years, recovery and rehabilitation can be said to be at the halfway mark. The journey to durable sobriety will be completed when they learn how to manage threats to sobriety inherent in associations with nonalcoholic drinkers, how to interact with people in all situations of stress, and finally how to proceed calmly and confidently through the labyrinths of their own minds.

Any consideration of relapse must take into account the elements that went into the original decision to stop drinking. The dynamic force of this decision must be understood by others and command respectful admiration. An alcoholic is usually a person in subnormal physical and psychological condition who knows better than anyone else that withdrawal of alcohol is going to cause pain and distress even less bearable than that which caused the compulsive drinking in the first place. Despite this the alcoholic makes the decision to stop. Those who think alcoholics lack will power should ponder those facts.

Improvement of physical, psychic, economic, spiritual, and social deficiencies is seldom immediate or sudden, although alcoholics may begin to feel better and obtain some small rewards for sobriety. Yet what is impressed most forcefully upon the alcoholic is that recovery and rehabilitation are going to require long term effort. The individual in the process of recovery is often beset by gusts of hostility and irritability, by caged restlessness, by insistent temptation. Often fogs of despondency and depression sweep in and no one seems to comprehend the alcoholic's need of a firm, confident guide out of the depressed state.

As the recovery process gathers force and strength alcoholics learn that it is virtually impossible to go it alone. Help of the right kind is necessary. It must be help tailored to the individual's needs and available when needed. Otherwise a slip is threatened. .

Finally it must be accepted that with some individuals a

slip is part of the recovery process. The alcoholic who relapses deliberately is most often testing the truth of what he
has been told—that he can't drink. He tries to find out
whether or not he can continue drinking—oh so carefully—
and keep it under control. The slip teaches him that he cannot.

CHAPTER EIGHT

Listen—Hear the Difference

As the accounts of Bill Barrett, Hal, Lisa, Don, and others indicate, alcoholism itself is complex, far-reaching in its effect, and has potential serious physical, psychological, and social damage. Its very complexity is often seized upon by alcoholics and their families as ample reason and justification for doing nothing about it.

Man's quest for a simple, reasonable cause of alcoholism has created more misunderstanding than clarity. Alcohol itself has borne the greatest blame, yet the inescapable fact is that not all users of alcohol, even excessive users, become alcoholics. Gluttony, one of the seven deadly sins, has been lashed from hell to breakfast, but even the moderate and almost abstemious who could never be called gluttons have become alcoholics. One can be secure if no alcohol is used at all, but there are other addictive behaviors as serious if not more deadly than the use of alcohol.

People have been using alcohol as a beverage for as long as they have practised agriculture, and probably longer. Primitive man is believed to have quaffed fermented juices of fruits, literally stump juice, long before he learned to cultivate cereals or carry home a piece of meat. Whether the effect sought from the use of alcohol as a beverage was revel of a ritual kind, or visions, or merely temporary release from the danger and hardship of the struggle to stay alive in a hostile world, alcohol worked quickly.

It is entirely reasonable after uncounted centuries of drinking, during which man has learned very little of the true effects of alcohol for those intimately concerned with the ultimate fate of an alcoholic to be alarmed, frightened, angry, demanding, protective or tried beyond endurance. They cannot comprehend the enormity of the complex problem if they do not fully accept the scientifically sound determination that alcoholism is a disease.

There is a further concept that has a bearing upon what man eats and drinks. There are individuals who, because of their physical activity, because of the effective way that they metabolize food and drink, and probably because of their environment, education, training and glandular balance can eat heartily all their lives and maintain a constant weight. There are others who may not eat as much who match in age, height, ethnic background, body structure and in all other respects those who do not gain weight, who nevertheless become obese. They wage a constant and usually losing struggle against weight. They become objects of indifference, pity, and derision. In our diet-conscious society the plight of the obese person is actually little different from that of the alcoholic. They are cursed by abundance and by the compulsive use of food. Nutritionists and endocrinologists are still striving to find the precise cause of obesity—the cause, that is, other than a diet imbalance. There is one slight difference, however. The obese person doesn't need to give up food altogether. The alcoholic has to give up alcohol, not only temporarily, but for the remainder of his days. No scientific proof has yet been presented that recovered alcoholics can ever drink again.

In the case of another disease long a scourge to mankind a means of controlling it has been found. The victims of diabetes who adhere strictly to diet and to indicated medication have a normal life span in prospect if they adhere to the regimen prescribed. But if they neglect the diet and medication necessary to control the sugar content of their blood they risk death. There are certain things they must not eat or drink because of the immediate and dramatic reversal of their physical condition such lapses of strict control may cause. The strict regimen necessary to maintain the health of a diabetic makes family participation and family understanding necessary. Treatment of a diabetic, except in the cases of individuals who are alone or isolated with no family ties, almost always involves at least one member of the family in addition to the patient, and usually all the members of the family.

Families share food and drink, a fact of significance in all the diseases that have any connection with the human intake of food and drink. The act of sharing carries with it a behavioral code and creates cultural and environmental considerations.

The environment of the individual susceptible to such diseases counts for very much more than many laymen suspect in the onset of the disease. The environment of treatment for alcoholism is of great importance to the individual undergoing therapy. The indifferent family, the indifferent doctor, the indifferent counsellor arouse hostility and resentment, just as the overpossessive and overcompensating individual who expresses concern is immediately suspected by alcoholics of being insincere.

If one is truly concerned about the excessive weight of an obese relative, the first thing one learns is that the obese person is a compulsive eater, unable to stop the intake of fat-producing food, drink, and sweets. To regain control of appetite they require not only the ability to limit their intake but also understanding reinforcement from those surrounding them—a reclamation from feelings of shame and inferiority.

If one is concerned about the diabetic patient in the family, certain daily chores ranging from the preparation of a special diet to administration of insulin or a reminder to take prescribed medication falls to certain family members. Not only does the diabetic learn to live with diabetes, but the family learns to live with a diabetic patient. There is no shame or inferiority, because the disease concept is well established. The alcoholic, however, is ridden with guilt, shame, and feelings of inferiority—a concept shared by their families.

Yet alcoholism is very little different than diabetes. There are ways of motivating alcoholics to reclaim their battered egos; to persuade them to cooperate in treatment. There are approaches that succeed in bringing about better understanding, mutual adjustment to a serious health threat, and slow but steady recovery from a handicapping disease.

All too often in the field of alcoholism one sees wives and mothers who with the best of intentions and out of misguided love are clinging to the oldest and craftiest infants extant, fighting off every possibility that their "baby" may become a mature person.

People attain their noblest stature when, alone and unaided, they face a decision or a crisis and bring it off successfully. All too often the alcoholic's decision or crisis or self-determination isn't allowed to come to fruition. Often the recovery of an alcoholic is due to a carefully tailored fable in which the alcoholic believes long enough to attain a secure plateau of sobriety. The chief fable observed in a long career of counseling alcoholics is that of the triumph of a recovery alone and unaided.

This is a very old and durable fable, and most useful. Not until several years of sobriety have passed and the recovered alcoholic can reflect upon the sequence of recovery do the various elements of the fable separate into a meaningful pattern.

In the first place no alcoholic truly enjoys the compulsiveness of drinking. They live in dread of the time when the inner static charge that builds up from bouncing over the frost heaves and ruts of life can be discharged only, lightning-like, by drinking. Alcoholics know very early in the process of their disease that they are in trouble with alcohol but they do not want to believe it. They want even less to have to admit it to another. Yet knowing that they are in trouble with liquor they become collectors of random bits of information about alcoholism, some of it accurate but most of it pure fantasy. It may seem strange but the fantasies get first call. Such foolishness as changing drinking patterns and residence and brands, switching brews, sweethearts, wives, and jobs is tried, and doesn't work. The compulsiveness is in no way alleviated. Once the fantasies have been tested and found unreliable an alcoholic may begin to heed useful information about alcohol and alcoholism and beget a good intention to try to stop drinking when a favorable opportunity presents itself. Somehow the most favorable opportunity—when the alcoholic is sick, hung-over, desperately in need of a drink—is seldom recognized as an opportunity, but appears more like an incontestable occasion for taking the hair of the dog that bit him.

In the course of the search for control of drinking there will have been various efforts to bring about a "cure." Such efforts will range from ultraexpensive sanatoria to being a guest at society's expense in custodial care. In each of these efforts the alcoholic learns a little bit more about his condition, a little bit more about what he can accept and what he cannot accept. By the time a big crisis occurs that can be used to motivate the alcoholic, he has a secret store of knowledge about alcoholism which he can use or not.

The most tiresome words one can hear from the relatives of an alcoholic are, "If he only would admit he cannot manage liquor!" What they do not know is that even if the alcoholic has admitted this to himself, he cannot possibly change anything by admitting it out loud. The alcoholic's chief concern is in finding out not how to manage liquor but how to get well without giving up alcohol altogether. The last element of the common fable of recovery by individual effort alone that the alcoholic surrenders is the notion that sometime, somewhere, and somehow he will be able to be a social drinker again. His chances are a million to one that this can ever be achieved, but one can measure the value placed upon the social use of alcohol by its users.

All the ingredients of the fable are awaiting the crucial moment when out of pain, confusion, desperation, horror— whatever the supremely moving experience—the alcoholic decides to make the effort to stop drinking.

If the first tentative groping for help is greeted by a warm, interested, and nonthreatening response, the bits and pieces that go into making up the fable fall into place. The wise therapist hopes the alcoholic will accept it because it is his own. From that point onward the alcoholic strives with a growing force flowing from his own conviction that he can and will recover by his own efforts. Actually his efforts will have been manipulated, steered, applauded, and modified by others. It often happens that an alcoholic doesn't truly know the reason why, after years of baffling failures, he suddenly accepts help and regains permanent sobriety, but those taking part in his effort will recognize each turning point, each recovery of slippery ground, each new foothold in the climb for the plateau.

The recovering alcoholic will usually resent those among his family and friends who become too curious, too intrusive in their efforts to assist. Families frequently are so amazed at the newfound replenishment of the alcoholic's determination to live without liquor that they show their incredulity trying to get into the act. If he is made to feel that he achieved sobriety only with the help of others upon whom he has been dependent he may deliberately relapse because he feels robbed of his personal achievement.

Slurs, criticism, preaching, nagging, quarrels, and the hostilities that have marked the upsets due to drinking are not quickly forgotten, either by alcoholics or those nearest and most important to them. An alcoholic has a real desire to make amends, but to do it with pride and without pressure. It is an unfortunate human failing to hark back to events and behavior better forgotten. It sometimes seems to nonalcoholics that living a day at a time and putting the past behind them is self-serving on the part of alcoholics, a convenient means of forgiving themselves their transgressions. But does one have to forgive the tubercular woman her cough, or the stricken cerebral-lesion patient his slurred speech?

There are many discrepancies in the stories told by those described in this book, including the accounts of nonalcoholic relatives. In each case the various individuals have been trying to give factual accounts of behavior, motives, events, and other relevant information. Yet the facts do not jibe because the viewpoints are different. Alcoholics relate the story as it has seemed to them, while nonalcoholic relatives, friends, or employers color facts by their own emotional response to behavior they cannot understand.

A truly altruistic and magnanimous person is a rarity. Similarly persons of perception who are capable of sticking to the facts and relating the facts with insight, one to another, are equally rare. And so, in counseling alcoholics one works with imperfect information. The best one can hope for is that the alcoholic, having been encouraged to disclose and verbalize inner thoughts and impulses, will reveal enough to permit the professional person to manage treatment with some skill. Or the need may be to make an intelligent choice of available community resources to solve enough of the alcoholic's problems to relieve the buildup of emotional charge.

To get at relevant facts requires tact, firmness, understanding, comprehension, and something very close to extrasensory perception. One must always keep in mind that the dynamics of the disease—the sweeping and all-inclusive compulsion to satisfy a physical and psychological hunger—

create a personality skilled at concealment, evasion, self-pity, grandiose fantasies, mock heroics, and desperate gambles. No matter what is going on behind the façade, the alcoholic struggles to give the appearance and impression of not being dependent upon alcohol.

Often it is not so much what the alcoholic says or confides but what is *not* said or confided, so that one maps the unknown areas of the individual's thinking by skirting around and establishing the boundaries of the unknown.

Success at encouraging communication with the alcoholic is more often a matter of listening intelligently and asking a minimum of questions while showing genuine concern. By the time an alcoholic individual has developed the disease to the point where almost everyone, even the alcoholic, is aware that a drinking problem exists, it is already too late for those near and dear to the alcoholic to attempt to talk it out with the sick person. Even with the purest selflessness they have lost a great deal of objectivity, insofar as gaining the confidence of the alcoholic is concerned. Hopefully they may retain enough objectivity to know that the alcoholic will communicate far better with a complete stranger. In the first place the majority of alcoholics are "surface" people, relying upon their often captivating first impressions to establish relationships with others. They will make an effort to impress someone they have just met, and if that person displays interest, understanding, concern, they are encouraged to give more of themselves and make tentative efforts to share their unease and anxiety and thus regain some of their lost tranquillity.

Many counsellors with long experience in talking over problems with alcoholics agree that they can almost "feel" the reaching out. It is a feeling that the alcoholic, striving so hard to seem bright and unconcerned, is silently imploring the counsellor to draw them out of the isolation in which they exist. It is a kind of aloneness that is worse than being cut off by time or distance from other humans, for it takes place in the midst of life, among people, with the sounds of life in civilized communities to remind them that they are solitary and apart from all others of their kind and class, that they speak and are spoken to but have no actual communication.

The unbearable solitude, if once broken by communication with someone who responds to their plea for help, is a refuge to which they can retreat if they are pressed too hard. This is the reasonable explanation for the experience with voluble alcoholics who are in their first phase of acceptance of help. They want to talk and talk, go on and on, as if they had been talking into a void until this moment, and one must be ready and even absorbed in listening.

To understand this volubility one should have an objective view of the effect of alcohol on human behavior in a social drinking setting and remember that the alcoholic who now, in a gush of words, is striving to recapture a safe and secure place with his preferred social group was once a social drinker.

Social drinkers—even the most moderate of them—display loquaciousness, argumentative casts of mind, disregard of the passage of time. They release the normal inhibitions that usually control their words and acts and are anything but reticent.

In the solitude of alcoholism all these desirable releases for timorous men striving to cope with the baffling mazes of life are withheld from the alcoholic who finds his loquaciousness branded as drunken maundering; his argumentation, hostility; his disregard of the passage of time, stupor; his extravagant talk, grandiosity; and his words and acts, aggression.

This need to talk was described vividly by a recovered alcoholic whose last big binge happened in Rome. "I had been drinking for weeks," he said, "and no one wanted me around—not my American friends, certainly not Italians who abhor drunkenness. I don't know how I did it, but I made my way at three o'clock in the morning to the Colosseum, and when the Italian police grabbed me I was screaming, 'Listen to me. Listen to me!' And you know why I was there? Not because it is an ancient and historic amphitheatre, but because I had suddenly remembered going there with a girl once by moonlight and I thought other lovers might be there and out of the capricious pity that those in love have for others not so fortunate, would listen to me."

Listen.

CHAPTER NINE

Community Resources

Within any given community one must expect to find a wide range of attitudes concerning alcoholism in the many health and welfare services encountered by alcoholics and their families in their search for solutions. Attitudes range from the extremely permissive do-goodery of rescue missions to the stark hostility of hospitals where the chronic police-case alcoholics have soured the outlook of overworked and underpaid caretakers at many levels of professional training.

It has always been easier to preach to an alcoholic than to help him to solve his problem. The alcoholic who seeks advice has been given the opinion that if he uses his will power he can "kick" the addiction to liquor. Will power has little to do with the onset of any disease. But in the preachments directed at alcoholics there has often been some reference to will power and backbone.

One must expect that dinning pat moral precepts into the ears of alcoholics can arouse morbid defiance and revolt against the morbid "goodness" of the preceptors. An alcoholic is usually powerless to fight back against the compulsions of heart, flesh and, most important, the compulsion of the dangerous substance that seems to right all the injustices and equalize personal inadequacies. Having fallen or been placed into the grasp of the self-righteous, an alcoholic slides, by slow degrees, into addiction. What is truly remarkable is that today even the most moralistic preceptors can perceive that by their attitudes they have contributed to the development of the disease. They often manage to keep their hands off the alcoholic until the individual is able to accept treatment, recover a feeling of worth, and is able to

135

walk proudly, once again the equal of those who stigmatized his disease.

This is not to say that the alcoholic is blameless and that society as represented by the community is at fault. Society must surely share the blame, but the alcoholic has known that the compulsive use of alcohol is stigmatized and has accepted those conditions in the use of beverage alcohol. It must be recognized that the stigma on alcoholism is also accepted by alcoholics as members of society. Such acceptance is the alcoholic's principal motive for attempting to conceal the disease.

By far the majority of people give only lip service to a more liberal concept that would make it possible for alcoholics to accept their illness without shame. Alcoholism is not hidden because it is incurable, which it is, or because it is difficult to treat, which it is. It is hidden because the only rationalization acceptable to the social drinkers in our society, who place high value on the amelioration of fatigue, care, tension, and inhibitions which alcohol gives them, is that those who become addicted in some way threaten their own moderate usage. They label the alcoholic as reprehensible and morally weak. The disease concept makes slow headway against this attitude because often the alcoholic doesn't behave like a sick person, but more like a wilful hypochondriac.

While there is a shortage of people trained in the recognition, motivation, treatment, and rehabilitation of alcoholics in the many community resources, one marvels at the degree of acceptance achieved in a short time through public education about alcoholism. Health and welfare agencies are acknowledging that alcoholism is a basic problem in a large number of cases and that whole families are not only involved in the disastrous effects, but must also be involved in the treatment.

One often hears today the comment that the spouse of

an alcoholic has realized and recognized that he (or she) is a part of the problem. It was long a mystery to many working in the field of alcoholism why they most often first made contact with an anxious relative and rarely with the alcoholic who needed help. It required time and experience to learn that this was the best possible contact; that it was better and more rewarding in the higher ratio of recoveries if the family members were first enlightened concerning what they had done to contribute to the severity of the disease and to make their contribution in changed attitudes and understanding to the eventual recovery of the sick alcoholic. Today the understanding spouse is a blessing, welcomed by the therapists, and assigned to a definite role in the recovery process.

Community resources prefer to work out the problems of entire families and not individuals, and so we find the total family treatment used in alcoholism gaining wider acceptance. The alcoholic, in short, is only a part of the problem, although the important part.

To consider community resources for the treatment and rehabilitation of alcoholics, compare what was available in 1934 with what has become available now. We can accept the testimony of the 1934 founders of Alcoholics Anonymous that, except for the very expensive "drying out" establishments, where the disease was treated under a variety of euphemisms and only to the extent of sobering up the patient, there was very little help the alcoholic could receive from the community.

The standard procedure in emergency rooms of general hospitals was a dose of paraldehyde. This was available only if the patient was lucky and didn't arouse the hostility of the personnel. If the alcoholic was in a coma (particularly during the Prohibition era) a routine stomach pumping was performed on the chance that the toxic condition might be due to poison alcohol. The death rate from delirium tremens was high. Internes and residents training for internal medicine were always relieved to learn that delirium tremens was a self-adjusting syndrome, which would pass if the patient lived.

There were health farms, usually equipped with all the gadgets of an athletic club—steam cabinets, masseurs, and a locked bar where the liquor was kept to be administered in tapering-off doses to alcoholics with the financial means to afford this "painless" approach to sobriety.

The psychological symptoms, if they became severe enough, were a passport to the quiet wards of most mental institutions. When families had their patience taxed to the limit, their thoughts turned to involuntary commitment of the alcoholic in a mental institution, or appointment of a conservator or guardian.

There were and are today the correctional institutions in which chronic inebriates, by court order, were dried out and desocialized at one and the same interval of custodial care. They were not considered to be sick people. The view most often expressed was that they were wayward and lacked moral fibre.

The very scarcity of facilities to treat alcoholism, and of doctors who considered alcoholism a sickness with a definite disease syndrome, and the lack of a basic concept that an alcoholic could bring the disease under control, made the fortuitous fellowship conceived by the originators of Alcoholics Anonymous an inspiration to alcoholics.

It was something more than a self-serving aphorism when Alcoholics Anonymous was founded that only drunks understood drunks. The shared misery of alcoholism gave them something in common. With the publication of reports of the success achieved by Alcoholics Anonymous, the flame of hope for all alcoholics blazed higher.

Two things were achieved by Alcoholics Anonymous— it provided an alternative to the dreadful quest for release from the addiction and, because of the undeniable success in recovery demonstrated by some patients who had made the rounds of the drying out sanatoriums, they aroused the interest in alcoholism of the medical profession.

The interest at first was casual, the observance of a phenomenon. Few physicians wanted sincerely to learn more about alcoholism or to accept a disease concept. There was an unspoken fear of becoming known in the community as a "drunk" doctor. Some hotel physicians knew something about alcoholism—not through choice but from necessity. Some psychiatrists studying the psychological aspects of the disease were examining alcoholism as a behavioral disorder, having long been puzzled by the human castoffs they saw in the mental institutions.

The fact that an old and conservative institution of learning, Yale University, began in the late twenties to study alcoholism and alcohol counted heavily in stimulating the interest of the public in a subject which had layer after layer of the prejudice of centuries encapsulating a small kernel of truth and scientific fact.

Americans have been observed to wage war on their health problems in a unique way, by voluntary associations of lay people who have convictions concerning a disease which they strive to bring to the attention of the public, the medical profession, and the sufferers from the disease. Alcoholism differed in one important essential from other diseases. Those who recovered from alcoholism had their lips sealed against proclaiming their recovery by the stigma of the disease itself.

The founders of Alcoholics Anonymous wisely insisted on keeping their fellowship anonymous. It developed through individual contacts, word of mouth, and demonstrated success.

Alcoholics Anonymous could not openly propagandize public acceptance of the disease concept of alcoholism and at the same time provide intelligent and enlightened treatment for the sufferers. They could only help one another. They could not seek public funds to finance treatment, research and rehabilitation. This was an important consideration when the voluntary organizations came into being at the end of World War II to wage the long public fight for recognition of alcoholism as a health problem.

Very early it was manifest that the voluntary organizations would have to choose a careful path, beset on one side by the "wet" forces and on the other by the "drys." The solution was to take a middle position, neither for one nor the other. Social drinking, the voluntary organizations held, was a personal matter, a free choice made by the individual. But alcoholism, a disease in which the individual no longer had a free choice, was a treatable disease and the concern of the whole community.

Today the community resources that have developed from the early mobilization of community concern and from the achievements of Alcoholics Anonymous are increasing year by year. While treatment for alcoholism in general hospitals is limited, there are sanatoriums and specialized A.A.-oriented treatment resources springing up in many localities. The care is generally good, the cost is not excessive, and the fraternal feeling engendered by association with other alcoholics in various stages of recovery has been salutary.

Halfway houses are also being launched in many metropolitan areas. The halfway house is a practical approach to the sociological distress and isolation of many alcoholics who have lost contact with families, friends, jobs, and communities. The name connotes half way back to society.

There are not enough of much refuges for alcoholics who are between custodial care and self-sufficiency to even make a dent in the estimated 3 percent of the alcoholics in the United States who are homeless and desocialized and who must by some means be reintegrated into the community. But they have achieved significant results for both men and women. The halfway houses have a simple approach and varied sponsorship.

In general halfway houses offer board and lodging at minimal cost to sober alcoholic individuals while they seek work or establish themselves in regular jobs. Most of them utilize A.A. affiliation as a supportive therapy and use the services of social workers, psychologists, or lay counselors to help the individual meet the many problems inherent in what is to the homeless alcoholic a radical change in his way of life. The objective is to retain the individual in self-sufficient living and reinforce his life with new habits of industry and sobriety. Some halfway houses are officially sponsored by welfare departments. Others, like the Flynn Houses, an experiment begun in Baltimore, in rehabilitation of homeless inebriates, are started on a capital of as little as five hundred dollars, managing to survive by pooling the money received from the individuals for board and lodging. They work by day and commune on a common, shared problem at night.

The same pattern is followed by halfway houses for women. Most of those who are taken into the women's halfway houses are on parole from correctional institutions, and the shelter afforded them gives them an opportunity to re-enter society by a slow transition from custodial care to firm self-reliance.

These resources, however, serve only the homeless and the desocialized. The other 95 to 97 per cent of the alcoholics in the United States find it somewhat easier to find and accept treatment, once they are motivated to accept their problem and cooperate in treatment.

For the alcoholic who acknowledges that drinking is an uncontrollable problem and is willing to cooperate in a remedial discipline, there are groups of Alcoholics Anonymous in virtually every city and town in the United States and in many foreign countries. They are listed under A.A. or Alcoholics Anonymous in telephone directories, usually on the first page, and many suburban newspapers publish A.A. ads indicating how to make contact. An alcoholic comes to a decision to take action and stop drinking, and the first step to recovery is taken when they look up remedial help.

For the greater number of problem drinkers the admission of a drinking problem is a matter for deep soul-searching. They are unwilling to admit even to themselves that they are unable to control their intake of liquor.

Most often they require complicated indoctrination before they take the steps to control their behavior and their addiction. In most cases of alcoholism the families, friends, and employers of an alcoholic are aware that something serious is wrong before the alcoholic expresses a need for help.

It is in this area of information and education that voluntary organizations have performed yeoman service. Information centers and counseling services have not only helped family members to make a rational and useful approach to alcoholism problems, but they also have quietly spread their influence into other community agencies which frequently encounter one phase or one aspect of alcoholism problems.

It has been found through experience over many years that in the majority of cases of alcoholism the initial contact with a remedial discipline has not been made by the alcoholic. Usually a family member or an employer seeks guidance. The need at the outset is for a basic understanding of what alcoholism is and what alcohol does to the alcoholic.

Community services of many kinds have good will and the best of intentions when faced with problems of alcoholism. Like many individuals closely concerned with alcoholics, they do not always choose the wisest course. Over the years the voluntary health organizations concerned with alcoholism have reiterated simple messages. Alcoholism is a treatable illness. Alcoholism is everybody's business. Early recognition makes the disease easier to treat. Alcoholism is not a moral problem.

These simple messages have had great impact. The need for counseling families has resulted in the formation of a subsidiary organization following Alcoholics Anonymous' principles—an organization for the nonalcoholic members of the family—Al-Anon Family Groups. In turn, Al-Anon Family Groups have sponsored and developed a fellowship called Al Ateen for the children of alcoholics.

The development of these fellowships to study alcoholism and to persuade families to take the proper action to motivate the alcoholic member are, in a way, a commentary on the failure of the American school system to properly instruct students about alcohol and alcoholism. Such down to earth information as the scientific fact that alcohol is not a stimulant but a depressant is unknown to many millions of young people.

Treatment of an alcoholic who has been motivated in the early stages of the disease to undergo treatment is complicated enough, but by comparison with the later chronic stages, almost a sinecure. Yet the employed problem drinker presents a complex problem. Family situations are usually precarious. Financial chaos may be found in the family exchequer. Children growing up in a disorderly family situation often present separate problems. Solution of these peripheral problems may spell the difference between a long and difficult recovery process and one that is comparatively uneventful. Family service organizations specializing in counseling on these marital and financial problems relieve the tension and the pressure on family members while the alcoholic is under the discipline of a healing therapy.

One area of imminent danger to the married couple beset by the alcoholism of one or both of the partners can be resolved by marital counseling, but one must be careful to avoid the untrained in this highly sensitive field. It is better to have no marital counseling at all than the irresponsible ministrations of numerous charlatans in this highly specialized service.

In the persistent effort to steer alcoholics toward acceptance of treatment there are times when a calculated risk must be taken in advising a husband or wife to carry out the often expressed threat to leave unless the alcoholic spouse stops drinking. But this action is one that cannot be left to the caprice of an unqualified marital counselor or even to a lawyer unfamiliar with the special situation involved.

Vocational counseling is of less importance in alcoholism than it was once supposed to be. There was a time, early in the development of industrial health programs on alcoholism, when it was considered that the "square peg in the round hole" might be a disturbing and causative factor in creating tension and anxiety. This, however, is no longer given so much emphasis. Alcoholics who remain on a job until the onset of the middle phase alcoholism symptoms when the problem is usually recognized are far enough advanced in a trade, profession, or skill to be fairly content with the job. The hostility, distress, and tension he feels stem from his drinking and not from the stresses of the occupation, even though occupational mores and manners may have contributed to the development of the disease.

There was a time—roughly about the time when in 1956 the American Medical Association took the step of officially declaring alcoholism to be a disease—when it was difficult to find a physician who would or could treat an alcoholic patient, at least for alcoholism. Even today there are very few doctors who devote full time to treatment of alcoholism. There are many reputable, skillful, well informed internists and psychiatrists today who can and will do something more than refer an alcoholic to Alcoholics Anonymous. This is not to say that any alcoholic can walk in on any doctor and expect to receive instant treatment and immediate recovery. Alcoholism is recognized by the medical profession to be a long term illness requiring long term treatment, and the education of doctors to treat alcoholism is also a long term project.

One area in which there is inexperience among community agencies is that of relapse. Too often they are chagrined to find that the individual upon whom they have lavished their skills has relapsed. Too often we expect the alcoholic who has depended upon an anaesthetic for several years to cease its use immediately and overnight become the kind of person he was before addiction set in. It is not so simple. Alcoholism is as insidious as the prejudice against it. Both grow with the years, but both can be overcome. In an unstable world the alcoholic gives up the use of the substance that has eased him past threatening crises only as a last resort.

Someone has remarked that an alcoholic is a person with both feet firmly planted in midair. Alcoholics are truly celestial wanderers, seeking orbits of their own in which they can grasp some easing of their psychic, physical, and spiritual pain. Not the least resource of the community is the clergy, and they are the most shunned by alcoholics. But it doesn't always have to be that way. There has been an immense amount of guesswork and experimentation with the alcoholic's immortal ingredient—the soul. Research activity carried on in recent years has established that a large percentage of alcoholics are estranged from their faith, or that they are faithless and submerged in feelings of unworthiness. Many have rejected their religious training, or rebel against even the mild discipline that religious worship requires.

One must consider that alcoholics carry a crushing burden of guilt, a deep-seated feeling of unworthiness that stems from the stigma on the disease, from the sometimes fanatical moralistic campaigns against alcohol, and from preachments that do not take into account the progressive nature of the disease. Out of the pressures that develop from these causes a skepticism, cynicism, and hostility to religion grow. Yet even the most advanced cases reveal a glimpse in the pervading darkness of their disaster; a tiny flame of hope —hope fueled by the vestiges of religious training that has survived all the physical and mental mauling the alcoholic undergoes.

Clergymen and church workers find alcoholics suspicious, hostile, or fearful. They find a bewildering variety of ruses to subvert the good intentions of the clerical counsellor or church worker. The alcoholic may have been pushed into seeking help from the church. All too often the experience necessary to achieving skill as a counsellor is not available to clergymen. In order to counsel alcoholics clergymen and church workers must first educate their congregations about alcohlism, with emphasis on the disease and avoidance of moralizing. Here again stigma has raised a terrifying barrier between the alcoholic and the help he needs and wants. Pastoral counsellors are shifting the emphasis from direct counselling of alcoholics—a hope for the future—to counselling in depth for members of alcoholics' families. Counselling and treatment of alcoholics is improved by having it take place in a neutral setting—in the community but not in the parsonage, the vestry, or the pastor's office.

It is useful at this point to consider the spiritual aspects of the A.A. program. No formal religious worship is implicit in A.A. affiliation. The Serenity prayer is inspirational. The Lord's Prayer is used at the end of the meetings almost routinely. Yet the appeasement of spiritual hunger is a foremost consideration. A.A.'s speak of God as one understands Him. And the twelve suggested steps in A.A. are in essence a restatement of the Golden Rule. One cannot deny that the vagueness of "God as one understands Him" is a definite yearning for the help of a power greater than themselves.

Reaching out for that power has undeniably bridged a spiritual chasm for many alcoholics.

Review of what has been accomplished since Alcoholics Anonymous offered dramatic proof that alcoholics can recover indicates that there has been a breakthrough. The inertia of adverse public opinion about alcoholism has been overcome and remedial efforts are beginning to move.

The most significant breakthrough, however, has been achieved by industrial medicine. As specialists in the medical field, industrial physicians seem to have learned more about alcoholism and the necessary treatment for alcoholism than their colleagues in the other medical specialties. They have provided leadership in public acceptance of the disease concept of alcoholism. In the context of an individual's employment and work achievement, which today is more a matter of record than it was a generation ago, it is easier to spot evidences of the forerunning and primary symptoms of alcoholism. Industrial physicians have very extensive employment and behavioral records available to them when they must make a determination of the difference between alcoholic employees' behavior and that of nonalcoholics.

In the beginning of the industrial alcoholism programs it was the large corporations with highly sophisticated and advanced employee relations programs that undertook to write company policies on recognition, treatment, and use of resources outside the company to treat their alcoholic employees. They had found convincing evidence that when an alcoholic employee was fired instead of treated the corporation threw away an asset.

Many more corporations—including middle-sized and smaller corporations with only a few hundred employees— are following suit today. The latter could not afford to take this step unless community services existed to help, refer, and treat alcoholics.

The industrial breakthrough was a tremendous achievement for those who urged the public to erase the stigma on alcoholism. Although at the outset the reasons for company policies on alcoholism were expressed in humanitarian terms, enlightened self-interest of both industry and the community has been responsible for the growing acceptance of such programs. The community is relieved of the added burden of caring for alcoholics and their families after they have lost their principal support, and the corporation saves an asset in retaining an employee whose training has cost the company considerable money.

Business and industry took the practical view that it cost less to treat and rehabilitate an alcoholic on the job than it cost for a replacement. The most convincing argument presented to one large corporation was that it costs less to keep an alcoholic under treatment and on the job than it costs to send a company representative by air across the country.

INDUSTRY

When one searches the histories of a large percentage of problem drinkers who have achieved recovery, a single factor can be discerned. Recovered alcoholics may have a cluster of motivations at work to ferment their desire to bring drinking problems under control, but the only one they hold in common is their desire to retain their job, profession, or livelihood or to establish themselves in more gainful employment. The other motivations in this complex are important, but none are so meaningful as the probability that if they do not control their drinking they will lose not only their occupation but also their status.

Personnel officers, medical consultants, and employee relations specialists as a group have an opportunity for closeup observation of alcoholism in business and industrial settings. On an increasingly wider area in business and industry they are providing the leadership in the fight against alcoholism that now hinges upon early recognition and treatment of the disease. When a more sophisticated public health policy evolves in the fight against the disease, this is a circumstance that may provide the means of routine intervention at very early stages of the illness and interweave the whole fabric of modern competitive society with all its stresses into a sound, unprejudiced program of prevention.

Experience gained thus far in employee alcoholism treatment programs has raised many questions and provided answers for a few. Recovery, for example, means something different to the employer than it means to a member of Alcoholics Anonymous. The employer wisely limits his standard of recovery to improved performance of the employee on the job, not on total abstinence. The employer takes the position that his employees have the right to do anything they please within the law off the job, but that while on the job they must perform efficiently and effectively. The results achieved in treatment of employed alcoholics kept on their jobs while undergoing treatment and rehabilitation have shown 70 percent and upward recoveries, and the employers' noninterference in the personal and private lives of employees has brought about total improvement and recovery within the meaning of the words as used by Alcoholics Anonymous.

The histories of both Hal and Bill are typical of those encountered by treatment resources in referrals from business or industry. The individual is either kept on the job, or only temporarily suspended, or is placed on sick leave while the acute problem is worked out and then kept at work while undergoing counselling, treatment and rehabilitation in community resources. Most often the extrication of the alcoholism problem from hiding drags with it other concealed problems of the family and finances so that a total approach is undertaken rather than remedial work on the alcoholism alone.

One assumption that often misleads laymen is that alcoholism affect only the unskilled laborer. The larger percentage of employed alcoholics are found among the semiskilled, the skilled, the professionals, and the management group. In fact, the loftier the status, the higher the percentage of alcoholism in the group, although the higher the status may be the more one finds that private treatment, frequently of the most expensive kind, has been utilized. There is a definite, but as yet unresearched, tie between the competitiveness of employment and its tensions, anxieties, and frustrations in our society. The word employee, as we use it here, takes in the entire range of employment in the United States, whether salaried, wage-earning, fee earning, or any other form of remuneration because the sole owner employing large numbers of people has been replaced by a complex hierarchy of management staffed by employees of corporations. The one hundred thousand dollars a year man is still an employee.

Indeed it is those employees who do not have a direct supervisor who show increasing rates of alcoholism—salesmen, travelling employees of all kinds, and management's decision makers. The latter can always find concealment in the very exclusiveness of their contacts with others.

The very earliest signs of alcoholism are visible in the setting of a person's employment, even before family members may take heed of the fact that something is amiss in the provider's drinking behavior. Absenteeism, change of personality, erratic work pace, and many more clues to trouble are observed first on the job, and owing to our cultural acceptance of certain kinds of behavior associated with drinking they are passed over by fellow workers and supervisors. The usual reason given for not intervening is that (1) it might happen that they too would have a bad day and (2) no one wants to be a stool pigeon. Here again we find stigma at work to make it difficult for the early intervention to operate. Yet it is on the job that the individual's functioning begins to break down; it is there that the breakdown is noted and it is there the cover-up persists, when family members are still unaware that problem drinking has the family's provider in serious trouble at work. It is seldom a great surprise when supervisors get a telephone call from the spouse reporting a mysterious illness has felled the employee. The supervisor knows that the real trouble is drinking.

The caretaking group, including personnel officers, medical directors and consultants, employee relations specialists, and others who make decisions whether to treat or terminate are becoming aware that the best place to assist the alcoholic employee is not at the plant dispensary, but in the community's resources. Their referrals are more effective because this makes it possible for the employer to take firm action on a question that borders on some very delicate questions of individual rights, seniority, pension rights, and other sensitive areas. Problem drinkers who are informed by their employers that help is available, that there is a choice of whether to accept treatment or suffer eventual termination, are faced with a crisis at a time when a crisis is what is needed to compel them to face the facts. If the problem drinker chooses treatment, which virtually all of them do (some to postpone the evil day), he is given specific referral to a specific resource and is expected to cooperate in the treatment or therapy. In all cases he is encouraged to bring his family and all the problems stemming from involvement in alcoholism into the total program. He is also given assurance that his job will not be affected if he makes a sincere effort to cooperate with the treatment discipline chosen, and this includes even possible relapses. While this may seem weak to the old time rugged individualist, one has only to consider that in many European countries alcoholic employees are placed on sick pay while undergoing treatment.

Before industrial alcoholism programs could become

effective, however, employers recognized that supervisory personnel, some of whom might have the problem themselves, would need training in recognition of alcoholism problems so that the programs could operate with some degree of structure within the organization. It was in this way that early identification of employed problem drinkers became one of the first concerns of voluntary health organizations.

Under their sponsorship an ambitious college extension training program was set up. Lecturers on all aspects of alcoholism staffed the course. Personnel men, employee relations functionaries, industrial nurses, and others attended the fifteen-week course. It was as thorough an education about alcoholism as any layman could ask. However, it was useful in only a limited way, because what industry needed at that point was not specialists in alcoholism counselling but a few simple guidelines that would permit supervisors to recognize certain signs, refer individuals to responsible officers of the company, and have them arrange professional treatment.

An intensive study by a treatment team consisting of a doctor, a psychiatrist, a psychometrist, a battery of testing techniques, a social worker, and assorted counsellors finally developed the guidelines so that supervisors knew what to look for. Once they had spotted a clustering of symptoms they could hand the decisions over to responsible company officers or functionaries.

The list of behaviors was simple and, when observed in clusters, almost infallible in indicating illness pointing to alcoholism.

1. Drinking in the morning before starting work
2. Hangovers on the job
3. Absenteeism (several patterns, including those on the job only half there)
4. Drinking during lunch hours

5. Signs of tension and anxiety-jitters, nervousness
6. Tremors and shakes
7. Use of breath purifiers to hide alcohol breath
8. Chronic tardiness
9. Quitting work early
10. Avoiding close contact with fellow workers and supervisors.
11. Long breaks for lunch, washroom, water fountain, files
12. Changes in attitude and behavior
13. Undiagnosed illnesses reported by family
14. Uneven work pace
15. Financial troubles
16. Grandiose behavior

One immediate result of this test group of signs was a rush of referrals of "hard case" alcoholics—those far advanced in the disease who had been covered up by indulgent bosses. After those problem drinkers (who had an unsatisfactory recovery rate) had been found, referrals leveled off. In the months and years that followed, referrals showed a slow increase of men and women in the earlier and more easily treated stages of the disease.

In some cases the cost of treatment is paid by the employer. In others the employee pays his own medical bills. Some plans use insurance to cover payment for treatment. Others use health insurance to pay for bed care in a drying out period, group insurance of another kind to pay for counselling or group therapy, and private funds to provide consultation with a doctor, psychiatrist, or psychologist, a marriage counselor or family service agency. No routine handling of payment for treatment has been set up. In this disease every individual requires a different kind of program, one tailor-made to his needs. There are some employed drinkers who go into an A.A. group and recover without any more than the usual complications. But there are others whose needs might be considered unusual who manage to recover nonetheless.

Employers become aware of the persuasive reasons for entering formal programs of industrial health measures to control alcoholism when they survey the performance of members of their organization. The cultural factor has been found to be important. The man who once made decisions with the slide rule is being displaced by a computer, just as production line operations are being programmed by electronic devices. This fear of becoming obsolete accounts for much drinking to allay tension. The competition for the few places at the top creates alcoholism problems. The high-salaried man pushed out in a merger and involuntarily retired in his fifties is cut adrift without much left of life.

The early estimates of the prevalence of alcoholism among employees ranged around 3 percent of the work force, although this was found to vary with industries and occupations. Madison Avenue might spill 10 percent of its men in gray flannels into the growing pool of alcoholism while a profit-sharing cooperative industry with a lot of contented and secure employees would have only a fraction of three per cent. Sales organizations, ulitities, newspapers, foundries, and steel mills show higher percentages. The high percentage groups were in all cases those groups in which a drinking culture prevailed—the three-Martini lunch, a hard-drinking history, a boilermaker to get quick action and restore the fluid balance.

When personnel officers considered that except for the time employees spend at home asleep one third of their twenty-four hour day is spent on the job, they took serious action to find some means of early recognition and early treatment. They found a well-established mythology surrounding employee alcoholism developed as our society moved into industrialization and mass production. The shoemaker's apprentice of Lynn who was given a dram of rum as part of his wages and thus became alcoholic was a spiritual brother to the man on the production line who had been completely depersonalized and became a payroll number, whose pride of achievement and workmanship was unrecognized. Intimate and meaningful contact between employer and employee was lost.

Many old time free enterprisers used to brag that they had no alcoholics on the payroll—they fired them. Others expressed doubt that alcoholics could stand the competitive pace. But they learned that alcoholic employees not only stood the competitive pace but compensated. There are always the fellow employees who will cover up because they never know when they, after a rough night, may need the help of the man whom they aid by overlooking his distress.

While personnel officers complain that no reliable means of screening incipient alcoholism exists, they have become aware that evading action is in the long run expensive. They are learning that the majority can be rehabilitated on the job.

Only a fraction of the number of alcoholics in the United States are unemployed or unemployable. Most of the early and middle stage alcoholics are holding jobs or positions of trust. Their efficiency and value to the employer becomes impaired so long as they are drinking, but not always so seriously that drastic action must be taken.

There are no Simon Legrees among employers. They are most often, either by personal inclination or by terms of a union contract, humanitarians whose hearts are where their firmness should be. Often they feel it more prudent to retire or bypass an alcoholic employee than to take action that will give him a 70 to 80 percent chance for recovery.

Those employers who have set up practical programs that utilize existing community resources find that the majority of their alcoholic employees exhibit on recovery better-than-average records of achievement and dependability after they have brought their problem drinking under control.

Warm-hearted sympathy for a problem drinker employee and covering up is neither helpful nor wise. Some employees who have had the boss lay it on the line quit. But the majority, given notice that their drinking behavior has attracted unfavorable notice, will rate a job more important than drinking. The argument that excessive drinking is no longer private because it affects employer and employee adds weight to the motivation to cooperate.

Absentee records have shown that alcoholics have eighteen to twenty-two days out of work each year due to their disease, compared to a national average of 8 days' absence from all causes. The alcoholic employee loses 10 days' work each year above the national average. If he receives sick pay during this time lost because of alcoholism, the employer has sustained a loss of two weeks' work. If there is no sick pay the alcoholic's family has lost two weeks of support. As an example this does not sound serious. Add to this two million alcoholics who work in business and industry—omit agriculture, forestry, shipping, armed services, and government. The billion-dollar hangover. The disruption of work schedules, inefficiency on the job, spoilage, disturbance of morale, and loss to the community as the alcoholic travels the long road toward dismissal is more.

The cost of recovery is less.

CHAPTER TEN

How to Get Help

If one makes a decision to seek help for an alcoholism problem—for oneself, a family member, a friend or employee—one must be factual.

Alcoholics and their relatives should disqualify themselves from *interpretation* of what the facts are. They cannot be objective. Alcoholics will go to extremes of self-justification or self-criticism. Relatives are much too close to alcholism problems to gain perspective, and they are too often part of the problem.

At the outset a neutral person or resource to evaluate the facts is a necessity. The immediate question will be who determines when help is needed. Help is needed when either the person afflicted or those concerned about that person begin to explain away excessive drinking behavior and changes in personality when a person drinks.

When alcoholics become capable of an honest and unsparing personal inventory they declare without exception that a time came in their drinking history, long before they ever became seriously involved in alcoholism, when they had uneasy feelings about their drinking, when they recognized that they did not drink like others in their social drinking group. Relatives will invariably say that they knew something was wrong from three to five years before they ever entertained a suspicion that the family member was alcoholic. Wives reported in several research projects that they willingly took part in a conspiracy of silence about the drinking problems, attempted to find reasonable explanations other than alcoholic behavior for the husband's drinking problem, and that it was three to five years after they had

first observed the drinking excesses that they finally admitted to themselves that their husbands were alcoholics.
And even then they didn't seek help, but continued concealment, withdrew from their social group, tried home "cures,"
none of which were of any help.

The research findings are borne out by practical experience with alcoholics. Husbands and wives are so busy in
attempts to make the drinking behavior of an alcoholic
spouse sound normal and reasonable that they do not take
the reasonable and sensible action that one would take with
any other illness—that is consult a professional person or a
resource that can be of help.

The time to search for a treatment resource is not in the
middle of the night when an intoxicated, emotionally upset,
and often aggressive alcoholic is raising ructions. It is far
better to make up one's mind to seek some help the next day
and not to put it off because the alcoholic then will be hung
over, repentant, and ready to promise the impossible. The
time to call the family doctor is not in the hours when he
needs rest, but during regular office hours and with the intention of talking frankly about the problem.

One must be aware that if the help is sought with the
hope and intention of hearing only what one wants to hear
and avoiding the unpleasant news that the trouble is alcoholism it is quite possible to find doctors who will be relieved to dismiss a vexatious problem so easily on the basis
of the biased information given to them by relatives, even
though they may suspect that the real trouble is alcoholism.

Actually, when one seeks help with alcoholism it is with
almost certain knowledge that the problem is alcoholism,
and if one has misread the symptoms and signs for any reason, the professionals will soon spot the error, for they are
much too busy and overworked to go along with an erroneous diagnosis. So don't try to put a stop to simple social

drinking because of moral judgments or bias against the use of intoxicants by calling it alcoholism.

Finding the most suitable treatment resource for an alcoholic is the crux of the problem in each instance. Facilities differ from community to community and often are as variable as the community's acceptance of the disease concept of alcoholism. But certain basic resources can be found everywhere and when properly approached will help to locate and enlist the essential service an alcoholic needs.

Taking the treatment step by step the first and most important consideration is "drying out" the alcoholic so that one can communicate rationally and reasonably with a sick but sober alcoholic. A person who is intoxicated is in no condition to discuss anything with good judgment and calm reason. Therapists experienced in work with alcoholics will never undertake anything but referral to a "drying out" regimen with an intoxicated alcoholic.

It is possible to dry out at home and in the care of one's intimate family or to sweat it out alone and unaided, but the process requires dedication and desperation, acceptance and understanding, cooperation and compassion. Families find themselves yielding to an alcoholic's pleas for a drink to straighten out the toxic condition by raising the blood alcohol content of the patient but never getting off this deadly carrousel. It is far better to find a hospital bed in a resource that has experience in drying out alcoholics if an individual is unable to go two or three days without liquor.

Physicians are aware of the location and cost of such resources. One cannot guarantee the results to be achieved by submitting to the sobering up process which so often passes for treatment of alcoholism when it is, in fact, merely an interlude between drinking bouts. Sobering up is only the first step. After that must come treatment which the patient can accept and with which the patient will cooperate.

One should not hesitate to ask questions when seeking effective treatment for alcoholism.

In every community of moderate size, down to the population center of every county in this country, there are low cost, voluntary public resources devoted to the health and welfare of all. Often several of these services are necessary to bring about control of an alcoholism problem.

Legal, medical, and psychiatric assistance are often free of charge to those who lack the funds, either through legal aid societies, free medical and psychiatric clinics, or services paid for by welfare departments of town, city, county, or state. Social service workers can advise on such referrals.

Tangled finances can be straightened out by appeal to the family service organizations, homemaker services, and friendly visiting services. In the latter case visiting nurses or public health nurses can often be of great help not only in suggesting referral sources, but also in home care of alcoholics undergoing a drying out process, or withdrawal symptoms, or both.

Some may think that financial problems are insoluble and that because the person responsible for the main support of a family is alcoholic that no one will take an interest or help. The fact is that even mortgagees who have undergone vexatious experiences in delinquent payments from alcoholics will most often accept a reasonable proposal to carry the mortgage or assist in disposing of the property at an advantageous price if they have assurance that the alcoholic individual is trying to cooperate in treatment of alcohol problems.

Homemaking services will cooperate in cases where the homemaker has to go out to work to tide the family over until the alcoholism problem is solved. This includes care of small children who can often be referred to day nurseries or be helped by extracurricular school activities. It is not enough merely to sober up the intoxicated alcoholic and give him the address or telephone number of an A.A. group leaving it to chance that the alcoholic's problems will be solved.

The almost universal availability of Alcoholics Anonymous groups in North America and many foreign countries indicates the existence of men and women in every community who have recovered from alcoholism. In the absence in one's community of a physician or a known resource with a developed skill in dealing with alcoholism as a medical or psychiatric problem it is best to seek out the nearest A.A. group, attend a meeting or two, and discuss the problem frankly with the people one meets at A.A. meetings. Nonalcoholics are permitted to attend A.A. open meetings. It is only the closed meetings at which nonalcoholics are barred.

One should use some care and judgment in choosing the A.A. member to give advice concerning the individual problem. A rough rule of thumb is that if the A.A. member has three or four years of sobriety and is not overzealous or two didactic about what A.A. can and cannot do for an alcoholic, one can expect reasonable advice. Each group, moreover, has a secretary with acknowledged stability and sobriety.

If public alcoholism clinics exist in the community one can expect professional help and effective referral procedures to be available.

One's family physician will be aware of ethical private resources to help alcoholics. But the existence of recovered alcoholics in almost every community provides at least a starting point in the search for effective treatment and counseling for alcoholism.

One should ask the informant chosen from this group of recovered alcoholics for several things. The first consideration will be a drying out resource. One can depend upon what the stable A.A. member says concerning drying out.

They have usually tried all the resources and have learned from experience which ones are good and which are only a means of tapering off from a drunk.

Another prime consideration is to get the names of doctors or psychiatrists who specialize in treatment of alcoholism or who have alcoholic patients in their practice. Conflicting counsel will be given concerning the skills and methods of such professionally competent people, but a great deal of the confusion arises from the motivation, or lack of it, affecting the individual patient. One must recognize that most physicians are not inclined to take on alcoholic patients because (1) they are aware how difficult an alcoholic patient can be, (2) they are ill-informed or only sketchily informed about the disease, (3) they are, from considerations of tact, personal or social relationship, and professional attitudes, reluctant to discuss with a patient what they look upon as a personality disorder outside of their professional sphere. Those physicians who do treat alcoholism carry on a practice covering a wide range of other illnesses. Doctors who give full time to treatment of alcoholism are so rare as to be extraordinary.

The motivation of the alcoholic patient is something which should take priority over everything else. This is often an adroit operation covering a period of months during which the alcoholic knows little and cares less about the plan to help or is not cognizant of the subtle nature of the effort to create in the alcoholic the desire to accept treatment and get well.

Families, friends, or employers seeking to take appropriate steps to help an alcoholic should first examine themselves and their own attitudes with the aid of a knowledgeable counselor. They should find out how much they actually know about alcoholism and give some time and thought to finding out not what they think they know about it, but how

little they know about it. This will entail reading useful literature or pamphlets about the disease. The information they
may get will often be the thread that leads them through the
complex maze of finding the right resources. Only common
sense is required to distinguish between outrageous claims
of miracle "cures" and the accurate facts setting forth the
basic information about alcoholism.

Very often a telephone call will start a chain reaction
that will lead to a final solution of alcoholism problems. In
general a discussion of an alcoholism problem with a recognized social service agency and specifically with a responsible social worker or executive of such agencies will
provide a starting point. One has only to ask for the name
and address of the nearest organization specializing in alcoholism problems to knock at the right door.

It is recommended that the first action should be to determine whether an information center on alcoholism exists
in one's community. If such a center operates within travel-
ing distance of one's home it is important to go to that resource, explain the problem as it exists, ask for information
and guidance, and then do the necessary homework to
tackle the problem constructively. It may be reassuring to
families to know that by far the larger percentage of people
who seek help with alcoholism problems are not alcoholics
themselves but relatives, friends, and employers of alcoholics.
The actual treatment of the alcoholic ensues, but this sometimes takes place weeks later.

It is important to know that in the field of alcoholism
the use of mental health institutions and correctional institutions as primary resources to help penniless alcoholics is
neither prejudicial or unusual. A period of custodial care or
involuntary drying out in such publicly supported resources
is often found in the medical history of many cases of alcoholism. In an emergency these are sometimes the only re-

sources available, particularly if the patient is undergoing withdrawal symptoms with all the terrifying hallucinations that mark the acute condition called D.T.'s.

There is a consideration, however, which must be weighed—whether the patient is voluntarily committed to such institutions. No accurate studies exist to determine whether the voluntary commitment provides better motivation than the involuntary commitment, but in personal experience those who have entered such resources from personal choice seem better motivated to make the effort to recover than those committed against their will. Yet what must also be considered is that those who wake up and find themselves in custodial care for a period of time reach a crisis in which they become aware of the desperate nature of their sickness and are thus motivated to make the effort to do something more about it than to dry out and wheedle their way to release to resume their drinking cycle. Here is another kink in the complexity of the disease, and an indication of the sensitivity of judgments that must be made about an individual case of alcoholism.

The greatest handicap that the alcoholic or the person concerned about the alcoholic must overcome is inertia. When the alcoholic is intoxicated and troublesome, tension, hostility, and emotion build up to a peak and both patient and those concerned about the patient want something to be done immediately. But once the toxic condition has been alleviated, the immediacy vanishes with the hangover and the old inertia looks into a rosy optimism that all will be well until the next binge. Thus the first lesson to be learned is that an alcoholic sober is still an alcoholic just as a diabetic in control of blood sugar is still a diabetic.

In the states or political subdivisions alcoholism programs paid for by public funds are administered by various departments but usually are under the control of either the State Department of Mental Health or Mental Diseases or the

State Department of Public Health. Inquiry at the State capitol by telephone can elicit this information, and a call with a specific request for referral to the nearest resource under such public programs will provide the needed information.

Although all general hospitals do not provide bed care for alcoholics, most will grant treatment to an alcoholic with a visible injury or with acute symptoms such as delirium tremens. It is wise to check with the general hospital in one's home area to determine whether or not treatment is available for alcoholism before entering upon a search for help. Many general hospitals which do not have bed care for alcoholics will have out-patient clinics for treatment, and most mental health centers, both public and private, will provide information, referral or treatment for some of the many problems arising from alcoholism.

People should not be repelled by the idea of getting help for alcoholism from a mental health resource. It is often necessary for the stability of the alcoholic and for complete understanding of the reasons why alcoholism has become a personal problem to get professional and scientific attention for the behavioral aspects of the disease. Recovery entails learning why one drinks compulsively as well as how to control the anxieties and tensions common to alcoholics.

One will find the best all-around referral at the voluntary health resources devoted to the information, education, investigation, and control of alcoholism. In the telephone book these are usually listed under the name of the city, county, or area as committees or councils on alcoholism, and virtually all of these voluntary nonprofit organizations are affiliated with a national body—generally the National Council on Alcoholism.

As an example, the Washington, D.C., area Council on Alcoholism takes in part of the States of Virginia and Maryland as well as in the District. The Greater Boston Council on Alcoholism, the first such voluntary community resource organized in the United States, covers an area much wider than Metropolitan Boston. So in seeking a telephone number in the phone book look for City, State, county, or area Councils or Committees on Alcoholism.

If one desires contact with Alcoholics Anonymous, the telephone number is usually listed on the first page of the telephone book. Many A.A. groups carry ads in weekly newspapers giving a post office box number and a telephone number.

Similarly the Al-Anon Family Group, which can be of service to relatives, is listed as such in the telephone book, usually for a central service office or a special telephone answering service.

One should not be shy or reluctant to discuss the subject with the established and qualified resources. Without complete information the help given can be only partially successful. While the general public may still attach some stigma to alcoholism, those working in the remedial field on alcoholism do not stigmatize the disease. They are not interested in who is an alcoholic and who isn't, but in getting proper and acceptable help to alcoholics. Alcoholism happens to all sorts and conditions of people. One can be almost 100 percent certain that every modern North American is aware of at least one person who suffers from alcoholism. Considering the general acceptability of social drinking the indifference of the public to the needs of alcoholics is unrealistic. In this enlightened age those who hide the disease can only plead ignorance if they continue to conceal their problem once they have accepted the fact that alcoholism is a sickness.

Alcoholism need not isolate anyone. The lost and lonely need only stretch out a hand to find the firm warm clasp of compassionate and skillful professional help. But such help is not going to seek those who need it and drag them against their will to permanent sobriety. Someone has to ask for the help, to initiate the action. To take the first step, even if one has mistaken excessive drinking for alcoholism, does not brand the individual for whom one is concerned. Those working in the field of alcoholism have far too much to do helping actual alcoholics to waste time trying to convince someone who drinks excessively but not compulsively that he is a victim of alcoholism. But it is wiser to find out which it is and rely upon the judgment of those who are prepared to help.

No alcoholic has ever been helped by having the problem hidden. No alcoholic has ever been helped by pretending that the trouble is something else. The foundation of firm recovery is based on a simple but—oh so difficult recognition that alcoholism is a disease and must be treated as an illness, and the recovery begins at the point where the alcoholic says, "Yes, it is a disease and I suffer from it."

Step by Step Search for Help. If there is a family doctor, request referral, or consultation with a professionally qualified physician or counsellor.

If there is no medical advice available, look in the telephone directory for any or all of the following listings.

Alcoholics Anonymous (A.A.)
Al-Anon Family Groups
Committee on Alcoholism (usually named for city, county, or region)
Council on Alcoholism (usually named for city, county, or region)
Division on Alcoholism, Public Health Department
Division on Alcoholism, State Health Department
Clinic on Alcoholism
United Fund, Red Feather, Community Chest (ask for social service)
Family Service Organizations
State Department of Mental Health

Mental Health Clinic
Medical Society—State, City, County, or National

Ask for information about treatment for alcoholism, education and information about alcoholism. It is best to disclose your name and address to these official and voluntary agencies. But if you prefer to remain anonymous ask how you can make a personal visit to talk the problem over.

In an emergency keep in mind that for both acute physical and psychological symptoms there are hospital facilities that cannot refuse emergency or first aid treatment. Telephone to your general hospital or have your physician make inquiries concerning bed care for an acutely ill alcoholic.

In communities where hospital resources are denied to alcoholics under that diagnosis keep in mind that acute gastric symptoms, kidney and liver diseases, stomach ulcers, and any visible injury qualify patients—alcoholic or not—for bed care. It is as dangerous to ignore acute withdrawal symptoms marked by hallucinations, tremors, and convulsions, as it is to ignore a head injury, an internal injury, or a fractured limb. In considering hospital care one must face the fact that few patients with money to pay for hospital care, even for alcoholism, are turned away despite the stigma on the disease which prevails in some communities. The alcoholic without means, however, presents a different problem.

In the latter category consult the local welfare officials, ask the police to take the sick individual into protective custody or make an effort to have someone with at least some knowledge of alcoholism sit with the sick alcoholic during the acute withdrawal phase. Many alcoholics have died because they strangled when they breathed in material regurgitated when nauseated. A.A. members will often help with these acute problems, but more often than not A.A. members cannot be held responsible in a medical emergency. A hospital is the best place for the seriously ill alcoholic. Police are very careful not to leave acutely intoxicated people unattended in a cell, or to ignore a visible injury. Many alcoholics have died in police stations in the past, and police have learned to get medical attention for the intoxicated person as soon as possible.

Seek out-patient care for alcoholics whenever such resources are in your community. Excellent out-patient treatment is available in the states where tax funds support alcoholism treatment programs. In general, except when acutely ill, alcoholics can undergo treatment as out-patients without interfering with their regular working hours. In fact, the greatest number of present day recoveries are alcoholics who have jobs, careers, families, friends, and homes. Inquire, first of all, for such adjuncts to public health and mental health programs to which everyone is entitled, either free or at a very low cost.

Medical societies in most communities, even down to the level of county medical societies, have information about where to go and what to do to get treatment for alcoholism. It is wise to learn who is the best *physician* in your area with that particular qualification and seek help.

If all the measures have failed to find help locally, write to the following, state your needs, and ask for referral:

The National Council on Alcoholism, Inc.
New York Academy of Medicine Building
2 East 103rd Street
New York, New York 10001

North American Association of Alcoholism Programs
323 Dupont Circle Building
Washington, D.C. 20036

170 THE LONELY SICKNESS

American Medical Association
Council on Mental Health
535 North Dearborn Street
Chicago, Illinois 60610

The General Service Board, Alcoholics Anonymous, Inc.
P.O. Box 499
Grand Central Station
New York, New York 1001

Appendix

Q. If an alcoholic has only to make up his mind to stop drinking, why can't he have more will power?

A. The problem isn't one of will power or of making up one's mind to stop drinking. Alcoholism is a disease. No disease has yet been arrested by sheer will power. Alcoholics are suffering from an addiction, which, with proper understanding and treatment, plus complete sobriety, can be brought under control. Making up one's mind is only significant and effective when an alcoholic has the reinforcement of therapy to support his decision.

Q. How long does it take to recover from alcoholism?

A. The disease is arrested but not cured. With the majority of persons willing to and able to cooperate in treatment recovery begins almost immediately. It progresses towards secure confidence in the new way of life without alcohol until the alcoholic can manage all the trials and emergencies which formerly created tensions, anxiety and efforts to escape reality. The time for recovery which can be considered secure varies from the immediate (as in the case of an alcoholic who experiences a "conversion"), to a couple of years for those who may suffer relapse during treatment.

Q. What's the difference between an alcoholic and a social drinker?

A. The alcoholic drinker becomes obsessed with drinking to relieve his physical and psychic pain. He discovers a medicine which only stimulates a need to drink more of the "medicine" used to tranquilize the deeper involvement. The social drinker attaches no special role to alcohol except as a social

171

lubricant and does not develop a dependence upon alcohol or even a need for it beyond normal social usages.

Q. Can alcoholism be inherited?

A. No evidence has resulted from scientific studies of inherited tendencies to indicate that alcoholism is hereditary. The genes do not carry any craving for alcohol. Environment, which is a very different factor, can condition a person to drink excessively. Sons and daughters of alcoholics frequently drink to excess because they have learned from their parents and from their social group that such drinking is acceptable. But, it doesn't follow that they will certainly become alcoholics. We hear about those who do become alcoholics like one or both parents, but we seldom hear of the great majority who do not become alcoholics and yet drink socially.

Q. Will I have to stop drinking entirely?

A. If you could cut down on alcohol and have only a couple of drinks before dinner, and if, maintaining this low intake of alcohol, your personality does not change, and if you do not feel any need for more than the before-dinner drinks you are probably not an alcoholic, because alcoholics lose control in one way or another if they drink. But, if your behavior changes after drinking (and you cannot be the sole judge of whether it does or not) and you cannot stop drinking once started without some external intervention then you will have to stop drinking entirely if you want to bring alcoholism under control.

Q. Are there any drugs that make it possible for an alcoholic to drink safely?

A. No. The drugs used in treatment of alcoholism are used only to alleviate the physical and psychic pain, or to act as a chemical fence to motivate the alcoholic not to drink. There are several types which when taken under doctor's orders will cause distress if one drinks any alcohol. But there is no drug to make alcohol less harmful to an alcoholic.

Q. Do alcoholics have to be hospitalized?

A. Only the acute cases who cannot get sober without it, or who are experiencing withdrawal symptoms which require bed care and intensive medication.

Q. Are alcoholics insane?

A. Alcoholics have mental and emotional disruption, and display abnormal behavior at times during or after drinking episodes. Usually it is temporary. Alcoholism is, among many other things, a behavioral problem. Under standard treatment many alcoholics benefit greatly from psychiatry, but psychiatrists treat many people who are not insane. In most multidisciplined resources for treatment, medicine, psychiatry, religion, group therapy and sociology are combined to unscramble the alcoholic's tangled life.

Q. Why do alcoholics abuse the people who try to help them?

A. Alcoholics have over the centuries felt the censure of stigma and rejection, and they live in a world that they feel is hostile to them. Those who most often try to help are those nearest and dearest to them. They feel that they should be understood by those near to them, and, because their raw sensibilities are on the *qui vive* for rejection and criticism, they may fly into a rage at some imagined slight or criticism implied by the offer of help and descend to physical or verbal abuse. But such displays only deepen the alcoholics' feelings of guilt and they isolate themselves even more to avoid such outbursts. The great majority of alcoholics when offered help by someone who doesn't condemn, doesn't criticize, doesn't preach, will accept it eagerly, while rejecting anything that those nearest and dearest offer to do for them. This is one of the reasons why families have to know and understand what goes on during the alcoholic's search for recovery. And this is one of the reasons why families should be willing to release the alcoholic member to neutral professional help.

Q. How can you approach a person you know is an alcoholic but who resists or avoids discussing it?

A. You can discuss alcoholism at a time and place when they will overhear it. Leave informative leaflets around where they can find them. Most alcoholics have a feeling of disquiet within them, and they know something is wrong with their drinking, even though they will not admit it. They become eavesdroppers, listening to conversations about alcoholism, peeking into leaflets and pamphlets even though they will not and cannot agree with what they read and hear. But they accumulate information which in the crisis adds up to their final acceptance that their drinking is out of control. The alcoholic recovering from a drinking episode is frequently so sick that any help offered is grasped. And when the alcoholic is sober but hung over one may find the opportune moment to suggest professional help.

Q. How should alcoholism be handled when discussing it where the children can overhear?

A. Alcoholism is a disease. There are certain diseases one does not discuss with children, but alcoholism should not be one of them. The wisest handling of this situation I have ever encountered was in a family where the children were informed long before the alcoholic father had accepted help that he was suffering from an illness, and all through the time he was under treatment the treatment of the illness was discussed openly. Today the father is president of a big corporation and the children are grown up, and they still say quite simply, "Daddy was very sick once. He is an alcoholic and he can't drink."

Q. Does an alcoholic know that he is becoming an alcoholic?

A. Most alcoholics suspect when they observe that their drinking is different from that of their social drinking group that something is wrong with the way they drink, but they do not accept the mental picture they have of an alcoholic— the stereotype of the Skid Row drinker. They are not always aware of the network of rationalizations they weave around their compulsion to drink, most of which are derived from the age old stigma on alcoholism and the peculiar code of silence that alcoholics learn to maintain about their dependence on alcohol.

Q. How can an alcoholic expect a family to put up with the behavior that disrupts the family while waiting for him to decide to do something about the compulsive drinking?

A. Alcoholics experience something that the family does not realize is so very apparent. They see their role as family members slowly but surely edged into the background. The alcoholics who made decisions for the family find others taking over the decision making. They accept this because it doesn't add to the tension and anxiety that burdens them. The family comes to think of the alcoholic as a nice person between drinking episodes, but demands less and less from the alcoholic member until at last the alcoholic is in the chronic phase of alcoholism, impossible to hide, impossible to live with. Families rarely think that it has all happened before their eyes over a long span of years while the alcoholic has slowly but surely lost the place once occupied in the heart of the family.

Q. What are the early signs of alcoholism?

A. The very earliest sign is a tendency to place too high a value on drinking beverage alcohol socially. Alcoholics tend to talk up drinking on every occasion. They prepare for a social event with a couple of drinks. They have one for the road. They prolong drinking occasions beyond the hour when everyone wants to quit. Blackouts experienced more than once or twice are an infallible sign. In North America the increase in tissue tolerance—that is the ability of the body to absorb more alcohol for the reward of slightly less euphoria (or sense of well being)—is one of the marked early signs. Colloquially, the person of whom it is said, "He (or she) has a hollow leg," has acquired tissue tolerance, and this in itself rather than being a sign of manliness or great sophistication is really a menace and a danger signal.

Q. What are the causes of alcoholism?

A. The cause is not known. To put it more picturesquely, alcohol isn't the cause of alcoholism, scientists have pointed out, any more than gasoline is the cause of automobile injuries. It is now believed by researchers that alcoholism is due to an abnormality in the way an individual metabolizes alcohol.

Q. Should an alcoholic divulge his problem to a new employer?

A. Yes, today most companies operate some type of program to help problem drinker employees. Usually one or two recovered alcoholics can be found in management who understand the problem. If a prospective employer is seriously prejudiced against alcoholics, a recovering problem drinker would be wiser not to accept the job. If the problem drinker is fully recovered, he may be of help to his new employer, both as an example and as an aid to other employees.

Q. Do alcoholics return to drinking after the novelty of treatment programs wears off?

A. Alcoholics seldom relapse if they have fully accepted a

program of recovery and are cooperating in actively rebuilding satisfying activities. However, it is natural for a person who has been dependent upon alcohol for a period of years to reach for this tranquilizer when he is bored, upset with unusual occurrences, or under severe emotional stress. One should not panic if the recovering alcoholic returns to the bottle temporarily under these conditions. This experience for alcoholics serves as corroboration that alcohol does not solve his problems, and he will look deeper into ways of preventing the occurrence himself. It is wiser to face this disappointment with calmness and encourage the alcoholic to return to his program with added confidence and knowledge.

Q. Is it more difficult to help a woman alcoholic than a man?

A. No, the treatment for alcoholism is the same for both sexes. A woman's social and psychic problems differ concerning such things as moral stigma, the home, children. When these are understood and separated, discussing alcoholism from the disease point of view is easier and just as successful with a woman.

Q. Is there any conflict in treatment programs?

A. Usually the conflicts are in the alcoholic or members of the family. Professionals discussing alcoholism with individuals in need of help will clearly explain the functions of therapies, as well as personally administering them. This is one of the reasons it is necessary to discuss alcoholism problems and questions thoroughly when seeking help. Most people seeking help with alcoholism problems expect to get all the answers in one interview, which is not possible either for the interviewed or the professional. The first interview is for the purpose of getting acquainted. Only a few initial questions can be answered and understood. Sometimes a relationship can be established to continue with the desired help. This is perhaps the most important step toward recovery for the alcoholic and those who will continue to live with the recovering alcoholic.

A

BT
ASHC

R   D. Whitney. With a
5   eacon Press [1965]
c

1. Alcoholism.   I. Title.